Foundations of Biochemistry

(for majors)

Third Edition

by   **Jenny Loertscher, Seattle University**
      Vicky Minderhout, Seattle University

published by

Pacific Crest
Lisle, IL

Foundations of Biochemistry

Third Edition

by   Jenny Loertscher   Vicky Minderhout
Department of Chemistry   Department of Chemistry
Seattle University   Seattle University

Layout and Production by Karl Krumsieg and Denna Hintze-Yates, Cover Design by Denna Hintze-Yates

Pacific Crest
906 Lacey Avenue, Suite 206 Lisle, IL 60532
630-737-1067 www.pcrest.com

Any opinions, findings, and conclusions or recommendations expressed in this material are those of the author(s) and do not necessarily reflect the views of the National Science Foundation.

ISBN: 978-1-60263-529-6

Acknowledgments

This book is the result of countless interactions with colleagues and students who have helped shape our view of what it means to learn and what it means to teach.

Special thanks to Dan Apple of Pacific Crest, who helped transform our view of teaching through the Pacific Crest Teaching Institute (VM) and provided insights and inspiration to make this book a reality. Thanks also to Jeff Stephens who authored many of the early versions of these activities.

Thanks to numerous colleagues for their thoughtful comments and contributions which have helped us understand how to shape materials to fit a broad audience. These colleagues include:

Cheryl Bailey	Tim Hayes	Terry Platt
Theresa Beaty	Bruce Heyen	Charlotte Pratt
Adam Cassano	Pam Higgins	David Vosburg
Colleen Conway	Angela Hoffman	Linette Watkins
Cheryl Coolidge	Robin Lasey	Hal White
Kathleen Cornely	Julie Lively	Susan White
Liz Dorland	Sunil Malapati	Adele Wolfson
Matt Fisher	Larry Martin	Corbin Zea
Michael Garoutte	Tracey Murray	
Pam Hay	David Parkin	

We thank Denna Hintze-Yates and Karl Krumsieg for their excellent work on the preparation of the books including drawing figures and editing.

We owe a great debt of gratitude to our students in biochemistry at Seattle University. They enriched our understanding of learning through their patient efforts and constructive and insightful comments. Their enthusiasm for learning was always motivating and inspiring.

Support from the National Science Foundation (DUE-0717392) makes it possible to further develop, test, and revise these activities; share them with others; and help others move to more student-centered teaching strategies.

Table of Contents

To The Student

Biochemistry is a vast and rapidly changing field. Therefore it is critical that students majoring in biochemistry learn to examine and process information, to formulate relevant questions, and to construct their own understanding of diverse topics. Although the sheer scope of the field of biochemistry may seem overwhelming to learn, you will quickly discover that you already have had experience with many of the concepts you will encounter. As the name suggests, biochemistry integrates fundamental concepts from general and organic chemistry and applies them in a biological context. Therefore, instead of starting from scratch, the study of biochemistry is largely about practicing and applying skills you already have.

This book is not intended to replace a biochemistry textbook. Instead, it is meant to be used in conjunction with a textbook while you work in a small structured group. By actively engaging with the material, you will build your understanding of biochemical concepts while simultaneously gaining problem solving and critical thinking skills. Working in a group has many advantages when studying an interdisciplinary field like biochemistry. Group members bring different expertise to the table. Some students may have experience with biology, whereas others may be experts in organic chemistry. Still others may feel comfortable with physical chemistry. By listening to each other and sharing knowledge you will begin to construct a well-rounded understanding of the topics presented. Furthermore, explaining concepts to group members will help deepen your own understanding.

Each section of the book is organized into three parts: assignment, activity and skill exercise. The assignment is intended to be completed before coming to class and will help set the stage for the in-class activity. The activity is completed during class time as part of a team. Your instructor will guide you and answer questions as needed. These activities work best when all group members start with the same level of exposure to the material. Therefore it is important to complete the assignment, but not start the activity before coming to class. The skill exercises are challenging problems designed to help you practice and apply concepts introduced in the activity. Skill exercises are generally completed after class.

This book is an invitation to take charge of your own learning. We hope it will help make biochemistry as exciting and full of wonder for you as it is for us.

Jenny Loertscher

Vicky Minderhout

Department of Chemistry

Seattle University

901 12th Avenue

Seattle, WA 98122

Amino Acids and the Primary Structure of Proteins

PRE-ACTIVITY ASSIGNMENT

1. Produce a reading outline for the chapter on amino acids and the section that introduces the peptide bond. ✳Commit to memory the structures of the amino acids.

2. Draw a titration curve for the amino acid lysine using the pKas of 2.2, 9.0 and 10.0 for the ionizable groups of lysine. Use the titration curve in Model 1 and its description as a model for your drawing. Label the buffering regions and equivalence points. Draw the structures for the primary species of lysine at all the buffering regions and equivalence points you include in your graph. You might find it helpful to answer questions 1 and 2 to complete this.

3. Define the term buffering region and describe how you could locate the buffering region on a titration curve.

4. Define the term equivalence point and describe how you could locate the equivalence point on a titration curve.

Model Titration Curve

The graph below is a titration curve in which a solution of NaOH is added to a solution of propanoic acid (HPr). (This type of titration is often covered in general chemistry.) At point A the primary form present is the conjugate acid (HPr). As OH^- is added, it forms water by combining with protons in the solution. This reduces the concentration of HPr and produces the conjugate base propionate (Pr−). The Ka for propanoic acid is 1.3×10^{-5} and the pKa for propanoic acid is 4.89. When the pH of a solution of HPr is 4.89 (the pH equals the pKa which is point B on the graph), the concentration of the conjugate acid, HPr, and the concentration of the conjugate base Pr− are equal. For acids and bases, it is always true that the concentrations of the respective conjugate acid/base pair are equal when the pH is equal to the pKa of the conjugate acid. This is usually called the buffering region. Point C on the graph is the equivalence point. At this point the molar amount of monoprotic acid in the original solution is equal to the molar amount of OH^- added, i.e. the equivalents of protons equals the equivalents of base added.

Model 1: Titration of propanoic acid with NaOH

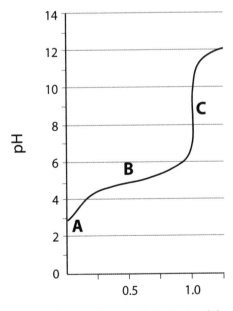

Equivalents of NaOH added

Why

Amino acids are monomers from which proteins are constructed. Understanding the structure and characteristics of amino acids and the peptide bond that covalently links them to form peptides will aid in understanding larger, more complex protein structures. Proteins carry out a multitude of different and important functions. The great variety in function is accomplished through a complex and variable polymeric structure. Comprehending protein structure will give you a better understanding of how proteins carry out their roles.

Outcomes

1. Use the acid/base characteristics (pKa data) of the 20 amino acids found in proteins to determine the charge of an amino acid at a given pH.

2. Determine the pI of a small peptide.

3. Identify the peptide bond and describe the structural features that characterize a peptide bond.

4. Use information processing skills to draw conclusions about chemical characteristics of complex molecules.

Plan

1. Form teams as instructed.

2. The person whose hometown is the most distant from here assumes the role of team manager. The team manager should assign remaining roles.

3. Answer the Critical Thinking Questions.

4. Prepare the spokesperson to articulate two discoveries the group has made that would help others better process information in this chapter.

Critical Thinking Questions

1. Quickly review questions a through c below.

    a. What is the letter on the model titration curve of HPr that corresponds to the point where pH equals the numerical value of the pKa for HPr?

    b. Is the titration curve horizontal or vertical at this point that corresponds to pH = pKa?

    c. What species of molecules are present at the point noted in question 1b?

2. The textbook values for pKas for each ionizable group of lysine are variable. For the purpose of this exercise, use the values of: 2.2 (α-COOH), 9.0 (α-NH$_3^+$), and 10.0 (R group).

   a. Will the titration curve for lysine be horizontal or vertical at the points where pH = pKa?

   b. What species of molecule are present at each pH = pKa value? Draw them.

   c. Using the pKa data for lysine, determine the charge on a sample of the amino acid lysine at pH 1, at pH 9.0, at pH 12.

      pH 1

      pH 9.0   → 50/50 mixture

      pH 12

3. From your reading and discussion, come to and record a common definition of pI.

4. While the definition of pI is straight forward, applying the definition is more difficult. Work with your group to establish the pI of lysine and finalize a drawing for the titration curve of lysine. Do not look in the book to verify your answer until you have made your own determination. You might find it helpful to examine Model 2 to establish the pI.

continued on next page

5. Refer to Model 2 for information relevant to this question. A sample of the peptide Lys-Glu-Ser has a net charge of zero between what two pH values? What is the pI of Lys-Glu-Ser?

Model 2:

The pI of a peptide is determined by examining the ionizable groups. The protonated and unprotonated forms of each ionizable group are in equilibrium. Consider the peptide Lys-Glu-Ser shown below at pH 7.2. The complete structure is on on the left and a stylized structure with just the ionizable groups is on the right. While the N-terminal is depicted as protonated, a sample of Lys-Glu-Ser is composed of a population of molecules and within that population some molecules may contain a non-protonated N-terminal group at pH 7.2.

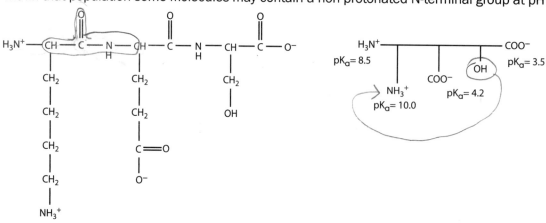

In the stylized structures below, only one molecule is drawn. However each diagram represents a collection of many molecules. Therefore "half protonated" implies that half the molecules present are protonated and half are not.

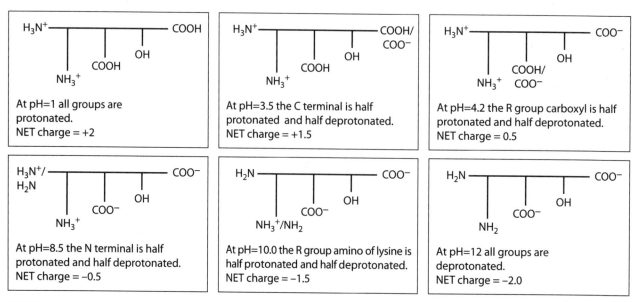

NOTE: In peptides and proteins, the N-terminal and C-terminal groups have different pKa's from the parent amino acid. The pKa of the N-terminal is about 8.5 whereas C-terminal pKa is about 3.5

Foundations of Biochemistry

6. Would Lys-Glu-Ser have the same pI as Ser-Glu-Lys? Explain.

For a rough estimate they would be the same but they will be a tiny bit different.

7. For a protein, how do you think you might estimate the pI?

find pH where it stops moving

8. Draw a dipeptide (use R_1 and R_2 for the side chain R groups) and the resonance structures of the peptide bond.

9. Recall the geometry about atoms that participate in double bonds or partial double bonds. What atoms form the rigid plane of the peptide bond (which atoms are coplanar)?

each le are a new plane

10. How do you expect the rigid plane of the peptide bond to impact folding?

The bond cannot rotate because of the double bond, so it cannot fold at this point ⇒ becomes the backbone

↳they can only fold @ the α-carbons

Section 1 — Amino Acids and the Primary Structure of Proteins

DO ON SEP. PAPER

1. Draw the appropriate titration curve for the tripeptide Met-Lys-Val on graph paper starting at pH 1 and ending at pH 12. On the curve label the pKas and the pI. Below the titration curve, using structures, show the equilibria that occur at the buffering region(s) and the equivalence point(s).

2. Draw the structure of the peptide Arg-Met-His-Val-Glu and label the coplanar atoms in one peptide bond.

3. Estimate a pI for the peptide given in question 2, above.

Foundations of Biochemistry

3-D Structure of Proteins

PRE-ACTIVITY ASSIGNMENT

1. Produce a reading outline for the chapter on protein structure. Your instructor will indicate how much emphasis to place on the Ramachandran plot. Try to construct a visual picture of the types of secondary and tertiary structures of proteins and understand what factors allow and control their formation and stability.

2. Use your book or another resource to identify the number of amino acids per 360° turn of an α-helix. Given this information, how many degrees of separation would you expect between each amino acid in an α-helix?

3. Consider the following peptide sequence:

Leu-Glu-Glu-Val-Phe-Ser-Gln-Leu-Cys-Thr-His-Val-Glu-Thr-Leu-Lys

   a. For the amino acids above, identify the hydrophilic residues by *circling* them and the hydrophobic residues by *boxing* them.

   b. This sequence forms an α helix. Create your model by plotting the position of each residue of the α-helix on the helical wheel plot below including the circles and boxes. The leucine has been placed for you at 0 (degrees). Continue to place the other amino acids clockwise around the wheel. Use the information in your textbook to decide how to space out the amino acids. NOTE: A helical wheel plot is a *two-dimensional plot* of the residues of the helix, as viewed along the Z-axis, projected onto the X-Y plane (you are looking down the main helical axis).

Model 1

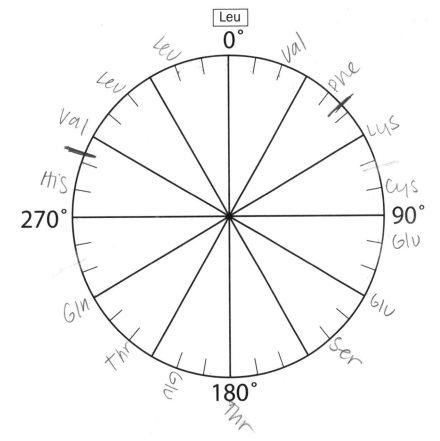

Why

Proteins are large molecules with complex three-dimensional structures. Since protein function is intimately linked to structure, understanding and describing this complex structure is important in understanding protein function. You will better comprehend the nature of proteins by understanding three dimensional protein structure.

Outcomes

1. Describe and identify the forces that stabilize the different levels of protein structure.

2. Understand and be able to describe the thermodynamic factors that direct and stabilize 3D protein structure.

3. Work in teams to build a model and use it to illustrate principles of protein folding and structure.

Resources for the Instructor

- One styrofoam cylinder per team; used to build a 3D helical wheel
- Red and brown pipecleaners cut into 2-inch or 3-inch segments

Place the first three pipecleaners representing the first three residues into the Styrofoam at 100° spaces—brown-red-red.

Plan

1. Form Protein Teams. Rotate team roles. Include a manager, spokesperson and two reflectors who focus on a behavior identified by the instructor.

2. Send a representative to pick up supplies from your instructor; he or she is your technology expert.

3. Answer the Critical Thinking Questions.

4. Reflect on your group's ability to work together to construct a model and use it to illustrate principles of protein folding and structure. What worked well? What improvements could be made?

Critical Thinking Questions

1. Review the assignment and come to group consensus on the placement of the amino acids on the wheel. (*take 3 minutes maximum*)

2. Recall from your reading:

   a. What limits the formation of protein secondary structures? (*take 3 minutes maximum*)

   R-group shape and charge

b. What are examples of secondary structure? Make a sketch of your examples.

c. What is the major force that stabilizes secondary structures? (*take 2 minutes maximum*)

3. Make a 3-D model of the peptide from the assignment using the styrofoam tube as the central axis of the helical peptide and pipe cleaners as amino acid side groups. Red pipe cleaners represent hydrophilic residues and brown pipe cleaners represent hydrophobic residues. The first three residues have been placed (or will be demonstrated) as an example.

4. As the protein folds to form its tertiary structure, which face of the helix (consider the one you have made) is most likely facing the aqueous solvent and which is most likely facing the interior of the protein. Explain.

5. What non-covalent interactions are involved in the stabilization of protein tertiary structure? Are the forces the same for quaternary structure? (*take 3 minutes maximum*)

6. What other interactions stabilize tertiary and quaternary structure? (*take 2 minutes maximum*)

disulfide is the only kind of covalent bond.

continued on next page

Model 2 The dimerization of two alanines to form a non-covalent alanine-alanine interaction in aqueous solution can be described by the following two processes and is depicted in the picture below. It provides a simple model for the protein folding process. *(Courtesy of Dr. Adam Cassano, Drew University)*

Process 1: Formation of alanine dimer from two free, solvated alanines

Process 2: Reorganization of water molecules from an ordered structure around alanine methyl groups to being part of the bulk solvent

In Model 2, water molecules with no lines are assumed to be part of the bulk solvent and interactions between alanine molecules are not explicitly shown.

7. Your group should label the bulk solvent water molecules, then complete the chart below

   a. Estimate ΔH and ΔS for each of the two processes given above ($<<0$, <0, >0, $>>0$, ≈ 0).

   b. Qualitatively estimate ΔH and ΔS for the overall process of alanine dimerization.

   c. Consider the equation $\Delta G = \Delta H - T\Delta S$ to discuss the overall thermodynamics of the process.

we know folding is spontaneous

bond energy

more likely close to 0

H-bonds
van der waals
dipole-dipole

	Process 1 (alanine dimer)	Process 2 (reorganization of water)	Overall Dimerization
ΔH	<0	≈ 0	<0
ΔS	<0	>0	$>>0$
ΔG			<0

   d. What is the biggest contribution to a favorable ΔG for the overall dimerization?

8. In proteins these alanines would not be free in solution but rather attached to other amino acids in a polypeptide chain. Using the model you built for question 3, imagine that one of the hydrophobic residues is alanine. Collaborate with a neighboring group to show dimerization of two alanines within the context of a 3D protein and make a sketch.

Foundations of Biochemistry

9. The term that is used to describe the biggest contribution to a favorable ΔG for protein folding (modeled in the preceeding dimerization) is called the *hydrophobic effect*. Explain why that name is a poor choice.

10. Have the reflectors report to your team.

1. The E2F family of transcription factors is important in regulating the cell cycle and has a role in cancer. These DNA binding proteins have conserved helix-turn-helix motifs that interact with DNA (NOTE: The DNA is represented as a stick diagram, whereas the protein is represented as helical ribbons.) Consider the protein α helix indicated by the arrow. This helix is approximately 16 amino acids in length and runs along side the DNA. Suggest a sequence for this 16 amino acid helix and provide a justification for your answer. Picture from Meinhart, A. et al. J. Biol. Chem..2003;278:48267-48274 (used by permission).

    View this skill exercise as an opportunity to practice scientific argumentation. Therefore the justification will be the most important aspect of your answer.

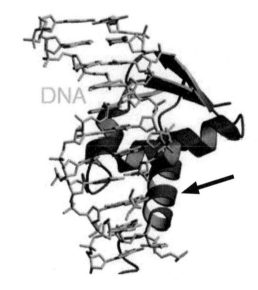

2. The Levinthal Paradox states that it is impractical for an unfolded polypeptide chain to randomly search all possible conformations before reaching its native folded state. This suggests that there could be a "force" directing the folding of polypeptide chain to its native structure. Finding the "force" has been the challenge of the fields of protein folding and protein structure prediction. The Anfinson experiments performed in the 1950's marks the first milestone of the quest to understand the principles of protein folding. It is usually referred to in most biochemistry texts and on the Internet. What is the Anfinson experiment and what did it reveal?

Foundations of Biochemistry

Tools of Biochemistry

PRE-ACTIVITY ASSIGNMENT

1. Make a reading outline for those sections in your text that discuss biochemical techniques. Also read the "Tools of Biochemistry Resources" handout. As you make your reading outline, be sure to include all of the items listed below.

   - Gel Electrophoresis -Determining the MW and number of subunits in a protein.
     - SDS and native gels and reducing agents like DTT (dithiothreitol) and 2-ME (2-mercaptoethanol)
   - Isoelectricfocusing
   - Chromatography
     - Gel filtration
     - Ion exchange
     - Hydrophobic interaction
     - Affinity chromatography
   - Amino acid analysis
   - How to sequence a protein
   - Protein assays
   - Immunological methods. These methods use antibodies. Antibodies are proteins that bind other proteins with high specificity and high affinity.
     - ELISA
     - Western immunoblotting

   Below is a link to an animation about affinity chromatography.

   http://www1.gelifesciences.com/aptrix/upp00919.nsf/Content/AD018C9E293F99BEC1256E92003E8 65A?OpenDocument

   (You can also access this page from www.pcrest2.com/fobc.htm or find it by performing a Google™ internet search using "ge life sciences affinity chromatography animation" as your search term.)

2. Watch the animation and make a sketch of the graph shown. Omit the red line from the graph. This line shows a characteristic of the buffer and does not represent measurements one would make in the lab. Be sure to label the axes of your graph. What is being detected in the broad gray peak? What is being detected in the narrow blue peak?

The broad gray peak is the molecules binding to the ligand and the blue peak is the molecules (proteins) coming off the ligand

Assay of Proteins

Total (non-specific) Protein Determination

These assays are performed to determine or estimate the amount of ALL protein in a given sample.

1. **UV Absorption** — Proteins have a characteristic absorption between 275-280 nm due to the presence of tyrosine and tryptophan residues. Extinction coefficients, however, vary by as much a 10-fold depending on the number of these residues in the protein. An average extinction coefficient can be used to get an estimate of the amount of protein present. The Abs_{280nm} is often used to obtain an elution profile (absorbance versus elution volume) during isolation procedures, especially during chromatographic procedures, since the method is quick, easily automated, and non-destructive. A disadvantage to this method is that other biomolecules, such as nucleic acids, also absorb in this region and can complicate the measurements.

2. **Colorimetric Reactions** — Several reagents have been developed that bind or complex with proteins to form colored products that can be measured spectrophotometrically. As an example, the *Biuret* reagent takes advantage of a deep blue complex formed between copper (II) and four nitrogen atoms of the protein backbone. The complex has an absorption maxima at 595 nm. Protein concentrations can be determined through comparison with standard curves prepared from a common protein such as bovine serum albumin. Each method has substances, often found in biological preparations, that can interfere with the analysis.

Specific Protein Determinations

For any purification or characterization of a _specific_ protein, some method must be found to quantitatively detect its presence. With a few exceptions, most proteins make up only a very small percentage of the entire protein in the source tissue. In addition, the protein of interest is very similar to all the other proteins in the tissue. Therefore, an assay for a given protein must be specific for the protein of interest and be sensitive enough to detect the protein at low concentrations. It would also, hopefully, be convenient enough that it could be used at each step of the purification process. The following descriptions are of methods that take advantage of some specific characteristic of a protein that makes it unique, identifiable, and quantifiable.

1. **Enzyme Activity** — As we will see, enzymes are proteins with catalytic activity. An assay for an enzyme that catalyzes a reaction with a readily detectable product can be easily developed. The enzyme reaction may generate a reaction product with a characteristic spectroscopic absorption or fluorescence that can be quantified. If the reaction generates or consumes acid, the reaction can be quantified through titration or by following pH changes. In addition, if a product is itself not easily measured, it may serve as a reactant for another enzyme catalyzed reaction whose product may be easily identified. These _coupled enzymatic reactions_ are common.

2. **Binding Assays** — Some proteins, such as receptors, are often assayed because of their ability to bind to specific ligands. In one method, a radioactive or fluorescent ligand is produced, incubated with the protein-containing solution, which is then passed through a protein retaining filter. The amount of radioactivity or fluorescence retained on the filter is proportional to the amount of protein. In a _competitive binding_ assay, a sample of the protein in question is made radioactive and a _known_ amount is incubated with a limited amount of the ligand. The sample with the unlabeled protein is introduced and competes with the labeled protein for ligand. Analysis of the amount of bound and unbound radioactive protein and knowledge of the binding characteristics of the protein-ligand can be used to determine the amount of protein in the sample.

3. **Immunological Techniques** — These techniques employ antibodies, proteins produced by an animal's immune system that bind other proteins with _specificity and high affinity_. This characteristic leads to methods that are both specific and sensitive. Two common immunological techniques are enzyme-linked immunosorbent assay (ELISA) and Western blot. ELISA is a specific and quantitative assay for a specific protein. Western blots are generally not used in a quantitative manner, but for examining presence of a specific protein.

4. **Bioassays** — Many proteins, like hormones, have specific biological effects. The effects on a standard tissue, cell, or whole organism can be observed and often quantified. These assays often require extensive development, may take considerable time to incubate, and give results that are less than reproducible because of the complex behavior of the living systems. Because of these factors, they can also be expensive.

Amino Acid Analysis

Analysis of the total amino acid composition is typically performed prior to sequencing of a protein. To do so the protein is subjected to complete hydrolysis in acid. The identification and quantification of the individual amino acids is conducted by an instrument that separates amino acids by chromatography and derivitizes them with an easily detected tag (usually fluorescence). The chromatography is typically cation exchange with a pH gradient starting from low to high. Each amino acid has a characteristic elution volume that allows identification and it is quantified by the absorbance or fluorescence intensity of the peak.

Why

In order to understand biomolecules, biochemists often need to isolate these molecules from the biological medium and, once isolated, to characterize them chemically. Many techniques are available to accomplish these tasks. In addition, biochemists have found ways to chemically synthesize some biomolecules. In understanding these techniques and procedures you will gain a better understanding of the nature of biomolecules, their functions, and how biochemists manipulate them to gain additional understanding of them.

Outcomes

1. Describe the molecular basis for some techniques used to isolate and characterize biomolecules in general, and proteins and amino acids specifically.

2. Select proper techniques or sequence of techniques to accomplish a given isolation or biomolecular characterization.

3. Produce a procedural flow chart for the progression of events required for sequencing a protein.

4. Use critical thinking and problem solving skills to identify necessary tools to elucidate aspects protein structure.

Resources for the Instructor

*   A computer lab or at least a room in which a or several computers is (are) available for viewing internet animations

Plan

1. Form Protein Teams. Assign group roles.

2. Answer the Critical Thinking Questions.

3. Prepare your team "Biochemical Toolkit."

4. Identify two ways in which your ability to solve problems related to protein structure has improved.

Critical Thinking Questions

1. Which technique(s) could you utilize to separate two proteins that (a) differ greatly by size, (b) differ by pI, and (c) that have similar physical characteristics (e.g. size and pI), but have very different functional characteristics? In each case briefly describe how the separation would be accomplished.

    (a) *Size affinity*

    (b) *isoelectric focusing*

    (c) *binding affinity*

2. On the computer go to the link *http://bcs.whfreeman.com/biochem5/cat_040/ch04/ch04xd02.htm* Click on the link entitled "SDS-PAGE Animation" and watch the animation. (You can also access this page from www.pcrest2.com/fobc.htm or find it by performing a Google™ internet search using "sds-page animation freeman" as your search term.)

a. One of the proteins in the animation contains subunits. How are these subunits associated with each other in the intact protein?

b. Imagine a different protein with subunits. This 100kD protein has two subunits (70kD and 30kD) joined by two disulfide bonds. Draw the gel electrophoresis pattern for SDS-PAGE with a lane that includes 2-mercaptoethanol (2-ME) and one lane without 2-ME. Be sure to include a molecular weight (MW) marker lane. Note: 2-ME is one of two commonly used reducing agents. The other is DTT (dithiothreitol).

3. Both SDS-PAGE and gel filtration chromatography are used to separate proteins based on size. On the computer go to the link

   http://www.gelifesciences.com/aptrix/upp00919.nsf/Content/281C4717F50A3605C1256E9200 3E865D?OpenDocument (You can also access this page from www.pcrest2.com/fobc.htm or find it by performing a Google™ internet search using "ge life sciences gel filtration animation" as your search term.)

   Click on the link entitled "Gel Filtration." Watch the animation. Imagine you have a mixture of proteins:

   a. If your experimental goal is to determine as accurately as possible the molecular weight of proteins in the mixture, would gel filtration or SDS-PAGE be preferable? Why?

   b. If your experimental goal is to collect each intact protein for further analysis, would gel filtration or SDS-PAGE be preferable? Why?

4. Refer to your answers to Question 2 on the assignment about affinity chromatography. What measurement was taken in the laboratory to generate these plots? Refer to the labels of the x- and y-axes to help determine what data were collected. What is being detected in the broad gray peak? What is being detected in the narrow blue peak? How would a scientist wishing to isolate a particular protein use the information given in the plot?

continued on next page

5. What techniques can be used to determine the amount of a specific protein in a sample? What characteristic(s) of the protein does each technique take advantage of?

6. Refer to the figure below.

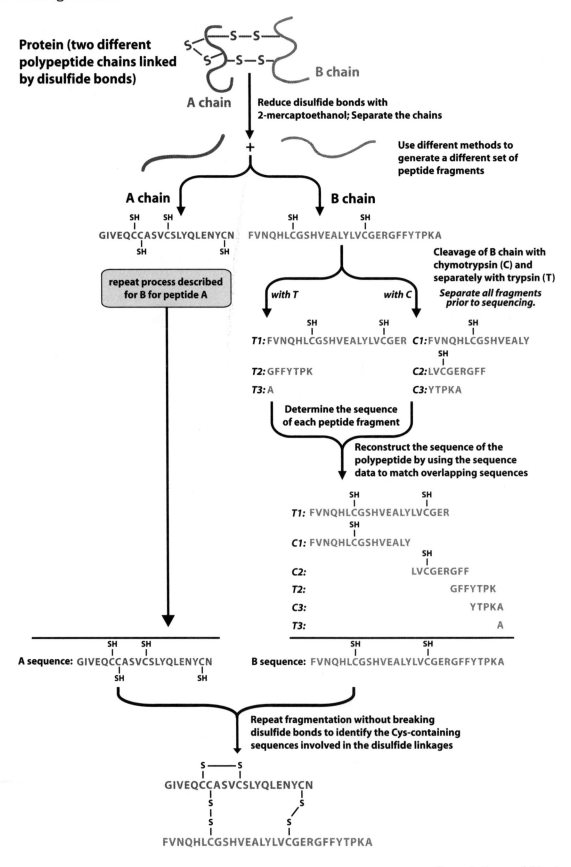

7. Prepare a procedural flowchart showing how you would identify the overall molecular weight of a protein BEFORE beginning the procedure shown in the figure in Question 6. It may help to consider hemoglobin as an example.

Gel filtration with standards; plot elution time vs. MW; run your sample to determine MW. Then run SDS(+/- 2ME)

8. Discuss the flowchart in the figure on the previous page so that all group members have a basic understanding of the procedures it describes. Be sure to discuss the reason why overlapping peptide fragments are generated and how this fact can be used in sequencing.

continued on next page

9. If your instructor chooses, you will have a follow-up activity that asks your group to use your biochemical toolkit to solve problems requiring the use of these techniques. Before that activity, work as a group to create a comprehensive biochemical toolkit. You may divide tasks for this assignment, but each group must arrive at the activity with one complete toolkit. Not all group members must research all tools for this assignment, but ultimately, all individuals will be responsible for understanding all tools for exams. For the upcoming activity, your toolkit should include:

    *   The name of the tool (technique)

    *   How the tool works (the conceptual framework for the technique)

    *   What the tool can be used for

    The toolkit should include reference to all of the following:

    *   Gel Electrophoresis

        o   SDS and native gels and reducing agents like DTT (dithiothreitol) and 2-ME, (2-mercaptoethanol)

    *   Isoelectricfocusing

    *   Chromatography

        o   Gel filtration

        o   Ion exchange

        o   Hydrophobic interaction

        o   Affinity chromatography

    *   Amino acid analysis

    *   How to sequence a protein

    *   Protein assays

    *   Immunological methods. These methods use antibodies. Antibodies are proteins that bind other proteins with high specificity and high affinity.

        o   ELISA

        o   Western immunoblotting

Problem-Solving Challenge: LWBGase

PRE-ACTIVITY ASSIGNMENT

Following a systematic method in solving problems improves the quality of the solution. In biochemistry employing a methodology is essential because issues must be decided and assumptions must be made before a solution can be proposed. Often times several different solutions are possible depending on the assumptions made about the problem (this moves beyond always having a single answer). As a result using a method to solve biochemical problems is recommended. In order to encourage you to try a method, the problem in this activity will be graded based on your method and not on your "answer." While the method is presented in a linear fashion it can be performed in spirals in which you move ahead and then circle back to the beginning to add new items to document your understanding. It has been observed that many students do not define the problem sufficiently and as a result end up solving a problem different from the one posed by the instructor. This can be especially costly during an exam.

Problem Solving Methodology © Pacific Crest, Inc.

1. Define the problem.

2. Identify key issues and determine important issues associated with the problem.

3. Collect relevant information, what is missing?

4. Identify assumptions.

5. Break the problem apart.

6. Generate solutions for the sub-problems.

7. Integrate solutions.

8. Test and validate answer.

9. Generalize the solution.

10. Communicate the solution.

The peptide shown below is acid hydrolyzed (6 M HCl @ 110 °C for 24 hours). The hydrolysed sample is then applied to ion-exchange chromatography on a column of Dowex-50 (Dowex-50 is a cation-exchange resin with strongly acidic phenyl-SO_3^- groups). The material eluting from the column is post-column derivatized with o-Phthalaldehyde, and analyzed by fluorescence. O-Phthalaldehyde reacts with amino groups to form amino acid derivatives. Draw a graph that depicts relative fluorescence versus relative elution volume. On the graph, label each peak with the name of the appropriate amino acid.

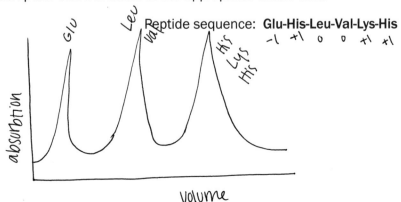

Peptide sequence: **Glu-His-Leu-Val-Lys-His**

RIP — Investigating Structure

The company you work for, Ramachandran Integral Proteins (RIP), has just isolated a protein, lakewobegonase (LWBGase), which they have found will make all women strong, all men good looking, and all children above average. In order to understand LWBGase and take advantage of its properties, the company wants to know something about the structural nature of the protein, **immediately**. Most of the procedures to get information about structure, X-ray crystallography, NMR, and sequencing will take time, as the company does not have these capabilities in-house and must send out samples to get this information. While the company impatiently awaits the results, the CEO of RIP sends out the memo that follows.

MEMO

TO: all techs in the trenches (that means you)

FROM: THE BIG BOSS

RE: LWBGase Structure and $

The person who can get the most information about the structural nature of LWBGase <u>in the next 24 hours</u> will get a big bunch of stock when the company goes public next week, as well as a life-time supply of LWBGase. Send all your information and data to the head honcho of the structural group for evaluation.

Imagine you are in a lab conducting experiments. You have at your disposal some standard biochemicals, an inventory of the standard proteins given on your protein MW ladder below, and various chromatography and electrophoresis equipment. Design sequential experiments to collect relevant data. After each experiment contact the instructors. Describe your experimental design to the instructor. If your design is correct, you will receive data from your instructor. When you think you have enough information, compose a memo to the CEO regarding the <u>structural nature of this protein.</u>

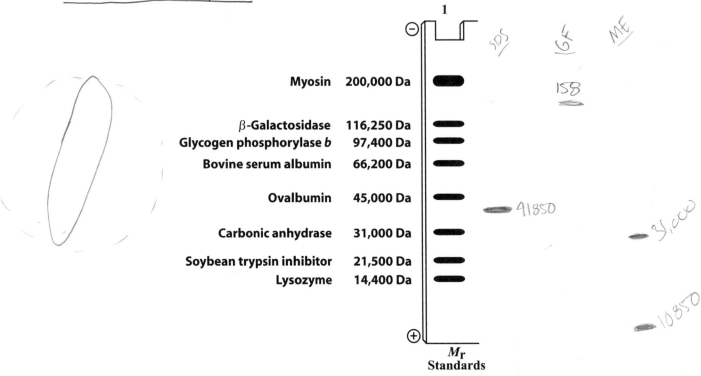

Myosin	200,000 Da
β-Galactosidase	116,250 Da
Glycogen phosphorylase b	97,400 Da
Bovine serum albumin	66,200 Da
Ovalbumin	45,000 Da
Carbonic anhydrase	31,000 Da
Soybean trypsin inhibitor	21,500 Da
Lysozyme	14,400 Da

M_r
Standards

1. You wish to separate and isolate four proteins from a cell lysate. Below are some known physical characteristics of the proteins. Design a scheme that would facilitate the separation of all four proteins. Depict your separation scheme using a procedural flow chart.

Protein	Molecular weight (daltons)	pI	Binding Characteristics
A	80,000	6.3	No Binding
B	40,200	7.8	No binding
C	49,000	7.8	Binds to concanavalin A
D	48,000	6.2	No binding

2. You worked on developing two skills in the activity: 1) problem solving and 2) communication. For each skill, list one personal strength and why it is a strength and one personal area for improvement and how you plan to make that improvement.

Problem-Solving Challenge: Working with Proteins

IN-CLASS ACTIVITY

Why

Without functioning proteins, all life would cease to exist. Protein biochemists wish to understand how proteins function in order to understand life. Thus, biochemists work with and utilize proteins in many different ways. By understanding how biochemists manipulate proteins, you will gain a better understanding of the nature of proteins. In addition, documenting problem solutions to these problems will sharpen your problem solving skills.

Outcomes

1. Use protein techniques you have learned to solve real-world problems.

2. Gain a better understanding of problem solving process.

Plan

1. Form Protein Teams.

2. Provide step-wise solutions to the "Real-World" problems.

3. Assess whether your group answers make sense. What criteria would you use to determine whether the answers make sense?

Real World Problems

1. The Investigative Proteins Group at Biodudes Inc. has recently isolated a protein, hangupthephone (HUTP), that the company wishes to pursue as a therapeutic agent to combat the seasonally-related outbreaks of "stupid driver syndrome" that afflict much of the population. The company wishes to produce the peptide through cloning techniques, but the first step in the process is to sequence HUTP so that a DNA probe, used to find the gene, can be manufactured. As head of the Protein Sequencing Group, your task is to design and direct the sequencing of HUTP. You have a cheap CEO and he bought a sequenator, but it is limited in the number of residues analyzed with accuracy (only eight residues are analyzed with certainty).

2. An important new drug, silverbulletophen (SBP), is being developed by Drugs-R-Us Inc. It was found in rat studies that SBP is metabolized to a potentially toxic metabolite. To try to determine whether this might also occur in humans, the company wishes to isolate the enzyme involved in the drug metabolism in rat livers and compare its characteristics with known human enzymes. As group leader of the Protein Isolation Team, you have been asked to design and carry out the isolation of the enzyme.

(This page intentionally left blank.)

Foundations of Biochemistry

Section 6

Hemoglobin: Protein Structure and Function

1. Produce a reading log for the chapter covering myoglobin and hemoglobin.

2. Find an oxygen binding curve for myoglobin in your textbook. How would you describe the shape of this curve? *has an asymtope. Increases quick at first then flattens out*

3. Explore the structure of hemoglobin using Proteopedia. Go to the Proteopedia site (http://www.proteopedia.org/wiki/index.php/Main_Page) and search for *hemoglobin*. On the hemoglobin page, explore the structures and answer the following questions. Note that you can rotate the hemoglobin molecule using your mouse and that clicking on green links changes the image of the structure.

   a. How many subunits does hemoglobin have? What are their conventional names? *4 2α and 2β*

   b. Identify the oxygen binding sites on hemoglobin. How many oxygens can one molecule of hemoglobin bind? How many oxygens can one subunit of hemoglobin bind? *4, 2*

   c. Identify the central cavity of hemoglobin. Is it the same or different than the oxygen binding site of hemoglobin? *different*

4. Locate the picture of bisphosphosglycerate (BPG) binding to the central cavity of hemoglobin in your textbook or online. Bring a copy to class for use during the activity.

Why

Protein function is intimately linked to protein structure. Understanding this structure/function relationship is important in understanding the limits of protein function as well as recognizing that variation in structure will ultimately affect function. Many genetically inherited diseases are the result of the production of structurally aberrant proteins. You will better understand how proteins work by examining the protein hemoglobin, a well-studied model of structure/function relationship.

Outcomes Part 1

1. Describe hemoglobin's oxygen binding characteristics using a graph and correlate the graph with the protein's function.

2. Describe and correctly use the term cooperative binding/homotropic interaction.

3. Define and describe the use of the p_{50} value.

Outcomes Part 2

4. Describe how the change in conformation of hemoglobin caused by allosteric binding is important in hemoglobin function. Depict the effect of allosteric binding using a graph.

5. Apply your knowledge about protein structure/function relationship to predict how changes in hemoglobin sequence (structure) might lead to pathological abnormalities in hemoglobin function.

Plan

1. Form Structure/Function teams as instructed.

2. Answer the Critical Thinking Questions.

3. Prepare your spokesperson to share two discoveries your team made about the relationship between protein structure and function.

Model 1

The following figure depicts the oxygen binding curve for hemoglobin. Some textbooks use the symbol θ whereas others use Y_{O_2} in the formula for fractional saturation.

$$\theta \text{ or } Y_{O_2} = \frac{\text{Sites occupied}}{\text{Total available sites}}$$

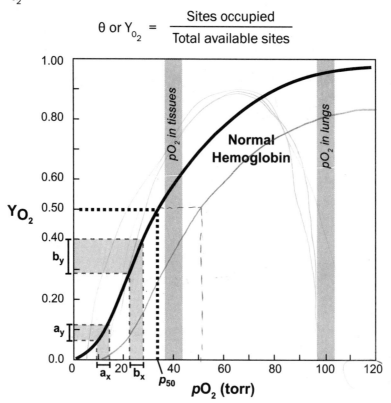

Critical Thinking Questions

Part 1

1. What is plotted on the x-axis?

    Partial Pressure free oxygen (gas) →above the solution

2. What does the pO_2 refer to in a solution like blood? In the blood, is there some O_2 bound and some unbound? What form of oxygen does the pO_2 refer to?

    unbound oxygen   *The bound doesn't participate with partial
    *related to the dissolved oxygen in the blood, unbound which is   pressure
     proportional to the oxygen in the gas above the solution.

3. What is plotted on the y-axis?

    Degree of Saturation of hemoglobin

4. When Y_{O_2} equals 1.0 how many oxygen molecules are bound to one hemoglobin molecule?

    4

Foundations of Biochemistry

5. For the change in pO_2 on the x-axis labeled 'a$_x$' locate the corresponding change in Y_{O_2}. What is its label?

a_y

6. For the change in pO_2 on the x-axis labeled 'b$_x$' locate the corresponding change in Y_{O_2} What is its label?

b_y

7. Compare and contrast the change in pO_2 (ΔpO_2) for 'a$_x$' and 'b$_x$'.

Same amount - or close at least

8. Compare and contrast the change in Y_{O_2} (ΔY_{O_2}) for 'a$_y$' and 'b$_y$'.

b_y is double a_y if not more

pO_2 air

H_2O

pO_2 soln

pO_2 soln ∝ pO_2 air

9. Using the data from questions 7 and 8, describe how the Y_{O_2} changes with increasing pO_2 levels and use the term "oxygen binding" in your answer.

* as pO_2 increases, The binding affinity increases at a faster rate.
* Y_{O_2} increases with increasing pO_2 levels because increases in pO_2 increases the affinity of O_2

Information

The positive change in hemoglobin saturation, Y_{O_2}, as more O_2 is present is called cooperative binding. More oxygen is bound (Y_{O_2}) for a given change of pO_2 at high levels of O_2 than at low levels of O_2. This shows that hemoglobin has a greater affinity for oxygen when the partial pressure of oxygen is high and has a lower affinity when the partial pressure of oxygen is low. The binding of oxygen at one site affects the binding properties of oxygen at another site on the protein. This type of cooperativity is homotropic since oxygen binding at one site is affecting oxygen binding at another site. The term homotropic is used because the same ligand, oxygen, is involved at the multiple sites.

10. What is the function of hemoglobin? Be sure to account for role of loading and unloading of oxygen.

To carry oxygen in blood. To bring oxygen to different parts of the body. Also carries H^+ and CO_2. Reversibly bind to O_2 (cells)

* always on/off depending on equilibrium of hemoglobin at that point/area

continued on next page

Section 6 – Hemoglobin: Protein Structure and Function

29

11. Discuss with your group how the shape of this curve communicates that hemoglobin effectively delivers oxygen from the lungs to the tissues.

It is lower in the tissues than in the lungs, meaning the hemoglobin releases O_2 in the tissue.

12. Explain why Y_{O_2} ranges from 0 to 1. What does your group think Y_{O_2} = 0.5 means <u>at the molecular level</u> for a sample of hemoglobin molecules? Draw pictures to convey your ideas.

Because it is a fraction of 0-1.

Y_{O_2} = 0.5 would be when 2 of the 4 subunits have O_2 bound to them and 2 are empty

$$Y_{O_2} = \frac{\frac{1}{2} \text{ sites have } O_2}{\text{total binding sites}}$$

13. When Y_{O_2} = 0.5, the value of pO_2 is defined as ___P50___ (see the graph in Model 1).

14. On Model 1, draw a new binding curve that is shifted to the right. Label the p_{50} on the new curve. How does the new value of p_{50} for your new curve compare to the original p_{50} value?

The new P_{50} value is higher → it gives up oxygen easier

15. How does the oxygen binding affinity for the "new" hemoglobin depicted in the right shifted curve compare with the original hemoglobin?

Binding affinity is lower

Part 2

Model 2

By convention the α-helical segments of each hemoglobin subunit are labeled A through H. The nonhelical segments that connect between helices are labeled AB, BC, CD etc., which refer to the α-helical segments being connected. Hemoglobin consists of 4 subunits named α_1, α_2, β_1 and β_2. The three-dimensional structure of the folded subunits is very similar even though the polypeptide sequences of the α chain and the β chain differ by more than 80% of the amino acids. The histidine labeled F8 in the figure below is the proximal histidine involved in coordination with the Fe^{2+} of the heme ring. In the α chain this is His 87 in the sequence, whereas in the β chain it is His 92 in the sequence. Both histidines are in the F Helix of their respective chain and therefore labeled F8.

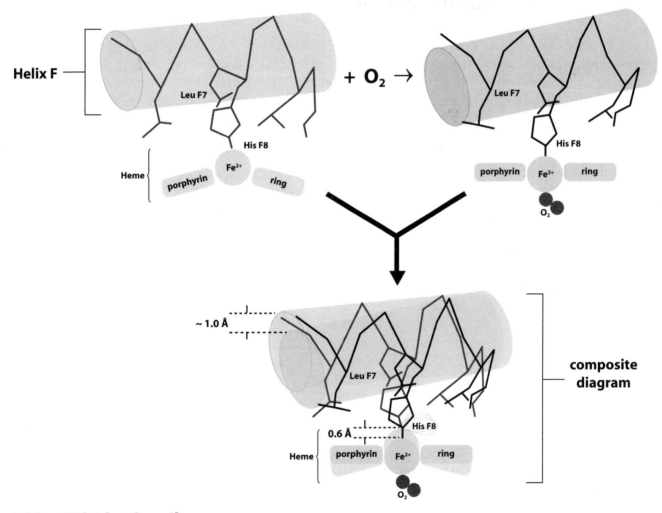

Critical Thinking Questions

16. Describe the overall shape of the heme group, (porphyrin–Fe^{2+}–ring) without oxygen bound to Fe^{2+}.

    bent

17. Describe the overall shape of the heme group (porphyrin–Fe^{2+}–ring) with oxygen bound to Fe^{2+}.

    linear

continued on next page

18. When oxygen binds to the heme group, by how many angstroms does the Fe^{2+} appear to shift?

0.6 Å

19. How far in Angstroms does the F8 histidine nitrogen appear to shift when oxygens binds to the Fe^{2+}?

$\cancel{1.0 \text{ Å}} \rightarrow 0.8 \text{ Å}$

20. Approximately how far in Angstroms does the Leu F7 appear to shift when oxygen binds to heme?

$\sim 1.0 \text{ Å}$

21. Approximately how far in Angstroms does Helix F appear to shift when oxygen binds to heme? What will happen to other helices in the subunit when helix F moves?

$\sim 1.0 \text{ Å}$. They won't move.

22. The binding of oxygen to the heme group results in flattening of the heme group and that event is communicated through the rest of the protein as Helix F of the alpha and beta chains changes position relative to the other helices and their respective subunits. This movement results in adjustments in the ion pairs at the interface between the α_1 and β_2 subunits and between the α_2 and β_1 subunits. The end result is a narrowing of the central channel of hemoglobin (the area in the center of the molecule). Therefore, structural changes within one subunit result in overall change in the quaternary structure of hemoglobin. Compare the affinity of hemoglobin for O_2 prior to the events described above and after those events. Make a generalization about hemoglobin structure as it relates to hemoglobin function. Your instructor may provide an animation depicting the described molecular events.

Affinity is greater when oxygen is bound. Structure changes to bind to O_2 easier

*changes subunit and others connected to it → cooperative binding

Information

In addition to O_2 binding, changes in other chemical conditions can result in changes in hemoglobin structure and function. Increases in blood H^+ result in oxygen binding curves for hemoglobin that are shifted to the right. The effect of H^+ can be understood in terms of the equilibrium:

$$H\text{-}Hb^+ + O_2 \rightleftarrows Hb\text{-}O_2 + H^+$$

dropping off

23. What is the pH of blood in the tissue and in the lungs and why does that difference in pH help hemoglobin do its job of delivering oxygen? Use the equilibrium equation in your argument.

More H^+ in tissues. low pH promotes unloading of O_2 into the tissues. H^+ binds to hemoglobin and changes the shape

Information

Bisphosphoglycerate (BPG) is an allosteric modifier that binds to the central cavity of hemoglobin. BPG affects hemoglobin affinity for oxygen by binding at a site different than the oxygen binding site and promoting a shape change in the molecule. The result of BPG binding is that oxygen binding curves shift right. When the small molecule is the same as the normal ligand for the protein this interaction is called homotropic as it is for oxygen and hemoglobin. The interaction of BPG with hemoglobin is heterotropic since BPG and oxygen are not the same and do not bind to the same site. *Shifts to right → binds more*

24. The molecule BPG binds to the deoxy form of hemoglobin in the central cavity. Explain why that makes sense for oxygen delivery and why BPG is said to stabilize the deoxy state.

Binding in central cavity → stops oxy state from making cavity smaller

25. How do the levels of O_2 in the atmosphere compare at sea level versus high altitude? Predict the blood levels of BPG for people who live at high altitudes, like Denver. How will those levels of BPG help their hemoglobin function better?

- low O_2 in high altitude so high BPG which lowers the affinity and allows O_2 to be dropped off in tissues

Multisubunit proteins

POST-ACTIVITY SKILL EXERCISES

1. In the mutant hemoglobin known as HB Providence, an asparagine residue in the β-chain replaces Lys-82. In normal hemoglobin, Lys-82 projects into the central cavity of the hemoglobin molecule. Predict the effect of the Lys → Asn mutation on the affinity of allosteric modifiers (relative to normal Hb e.g. HbA) and describe the effect the mutation would have on the function (oxygen binding) of HB Providence.

2. Under appropriate conditions, hemoglobin dissociates into its four subunits. Isolated α subunits bind oxygen, but the O_2 saturation curve is hyperbolic instead of sigmoidal. In addition, the saturation curve is not affected by the presence of H^+, CO_2, or BPG. What do these observations indicate about the **cooperativity** and **allosterism** observed in hemoglobin?

Assignment: Section 7

① $K = Ae^{-Ea/RT}$

K = rate constant
A = prefactor
$e = e$
E_a = activation energy
R = gas constant
T = temp

② $E + S \rightleftharpoons ES \rightleftharpoons EP \rightleftharpoons E + P$

$E + S \rightleftharpoons \cancel{E}S^* \rightleftharpoons E + P$ ES is more stable

③ $E + S$ requires more energy, but ES has more potential energy
$E + S$ is more thermodynamically stable

④
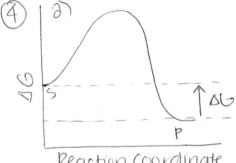

a)

ΔG (vertical axis)

S

↑ ΔG

P

Reaction coordinate

b)

S ES EP   ↑ ΔG

P

Reaction coordinate

✓

⑤ -Bring substrates together so they can react
-non-covalent interactions that speed energy of activation
-make/allow for intermediates
-provide a new, lower-energy path

Section 7

Enzyme Catalysis

1. Produce a reading log for the sections in your text that cover the general discussion of catalysis focusing on transition state stabilization. Find the Arrhenius equation in a general chemistry text, write it down and define each term.

2. Write a chemical reaction of the enzyme, E binding to the substrate, S. Write a similar reaction for the binding of the enzyme, E to the transition state, $S^‡$.

3. If binding is a favorable process, then what is the energy relationship between a) E + S, and b) ES; Which is more stable thermodynamically a) E + S, or b) ES?

4. Draw a ΔG versus reaction coordinate plot to show the relative energy levels of a) E + S, and b) ES.

5. Using the examples given in the text of how enzymes catalyze reactions, make a list of what enzymes do that allow the reactions to proceed faster.

Why

Virtually all reactions in biological systems are facilitated by enzymes acting as catalysts. Understanding how enzymes can catalyze reactions is fundamental to biochemistry. You will better understand how enzymes work by first reviewing some of the conditions that improve reaction rates in non-enzymatically catalyzed reactions and then recognizing that these principles also apply in enzyme catalyzed reactions.

Outcomes

1. Apply your understanding of intermolecular forces to rate enhancement.

2. Explain general acid-base catalyzed reaction and apply to enzyme catalyzed reactions.

3. Generalize your understanding of rate enhancement of an acid/base catalyzed reaction to other types of enzyme-mediated catalysis.

4. Integrate your understanding of rate enhancement and rate determining step in ΔG versus reaction coordinate diagrams.

Plan

1. Form Structure/Function teams. Designate a new manager. One person should take both the skeptic and spokesperson roles. Other roles as usual.

2. Answer the Critical Thinking Questions.

3. Assess how well your group persisted when faced with very challenging questions. If your group worked through difficult questions, identify strategies you used. If your group was stymied by difficult questions, discuss strategies you could use to make more progress in the future.

Critical Thinking Questions

1. Review question 2 through 4 of your assignment. Make sure everyone agrees. Reproduce the graph for question 4 in the assignment. Compare your drawing to the one below. If they do not match, discuss why this might be.

2. For catalysis to occur, the binding of the enzyme to the transition state is more favorable than the binding of the enzyme to the substrate. Using your graph for question 1, plot a separate G versus reaction coordinate curve on the same set of axes to show the relative energy levels of a) E + S‡, and b) ES‡ where S‡ is the transition state. NOTE: Although the transition state is hypothetical and not a real molecule, it is still helpful to include it in these graphs.

3. Label where a) E + S, and b) ES are shown on the graph at right.

4. Label where E + S‡ would be included on the graph at right.

5. Discuss how the graph at right indicates that optimal binding interactions occur between the enzyme and the transition state rather than between the enzyme and the substrate.

   ΔG is larger

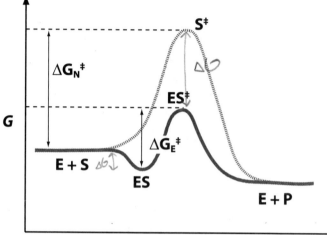

Reaction coordinate

6. Explain why transition state analogs are potent inhibitors of enzymes.

   Because they will bind with the enzyme instead of the S‡
   ↳competitive inhibition

Information

Recall that the rate of a reaction, R, for a first order reaction is equal to k[A], where k is the rate constant and A is a reactant.

7. Use the Arrhenius equation recorded in your assignment to <u>briefly</u> discuss each term. According to the following equation, (which can be derived from the Arrhenius equation) the ratio of the rate constants of the catalyzed reaction, k_E, and the uncatalyzed reaction, k_N is expressed

$$\frac{k_E}{k_N} = e^{[(\Delta G_N^{\ddagger} - \Delta G_E^{\ddagger})/RT]} \qquad \text{the term } (\Delta G_N^{\ddagger} - \Delta G_E^{\ddagger}) = \Delta\Delta G_{cat}^{\ddagger}$$

A rate enhancement of 10^6 requires that the enzyme bind its transition state complex with higher affinity than its substrate. Calculate the $\Delta\Delta G_{cat}^{\ddagger}$ that corresponds to a 10^6 rate enhancement of catalytic rate over non-catalytic rate at room temperature.

8. Below is a table of the common intermolecular forces encountered in the active sites of enzymes.

Nonbonding Intermolecular interaction	kJ/mol
H-bond	10–40
dipole-dipole	5–25
Dispersion	0.5–40

Using your value obtained from question 7, indicate how many H-bonds, or dipole-dipole interactions would be required in order to achieve a catalytic rate enhancement of 10^6 .

9. The figure below is an example of the keto-enol tautomerization seen in the rearrangement of many sugars of biological interest including glyceraldehyde-3-phosphate catalyzed by triosephosphate isomerase. The first diagram is that of the uncatalyzed reaction which occurs quite slowly, while the second is an example of general acid catalysis (HA) and the third is an example of general base catalysis (B). In general acid catalysis a partial proton transfer from a Bronsted acid lowers the free energy of the transition state by stabilizing the growing negative charge on the oxygen of the enolate. Discuss the stabilization provided for general base catalysis.

*acids + bases will be amino acid side chains

10. Generalize the observations and discoveries you have made today about catalysis, by comparing to the examples above:

a. catalysis that involves covalent bond formation and its effect on transition state stabilization.

b. catalysis that involves metal ions that electrostatically stabilize or shield negative charges and the effect on transition state stabilization.

11. Make sure everyone in your team can explain how the figure in question 5 of this activity demonstrates the preferential binding of the enzyme to the transition state over the binding of the enzyme to the starting substrate and write a sentence describing this.

POST-ACTIVITY SKILL EXERCISES

Consider the two reaction mechanisms shown below. Reaction 1 is uncatalyzed and reaction 2 is catalyzed in the active site on an enzyme. Answer questions a) through c) below, regarding these two reactions.

Reaction 1 (uncatalyzed): *NOTE that the lower product of the two products formed is also present in that form at the stage labeled "intermediate state", meaning it is the FIRST product formed, call it P_1. Only the intermediate state associated with the upper product (or second product) is shown below.*

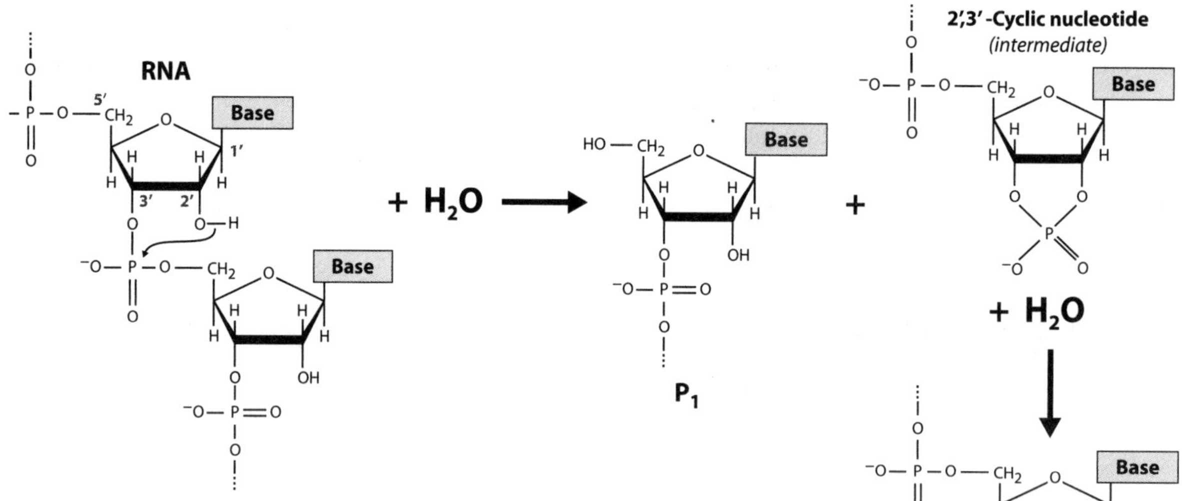

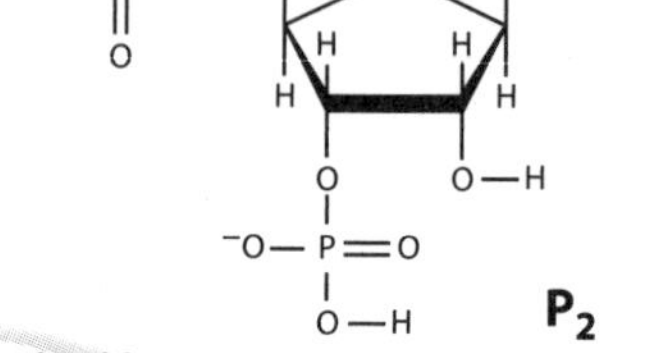

Reaction 2 (catalyzed):

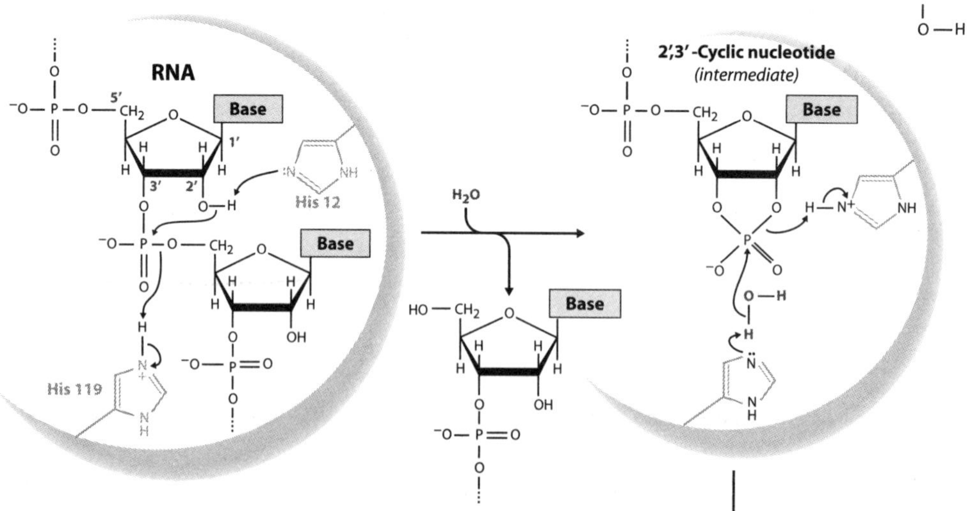

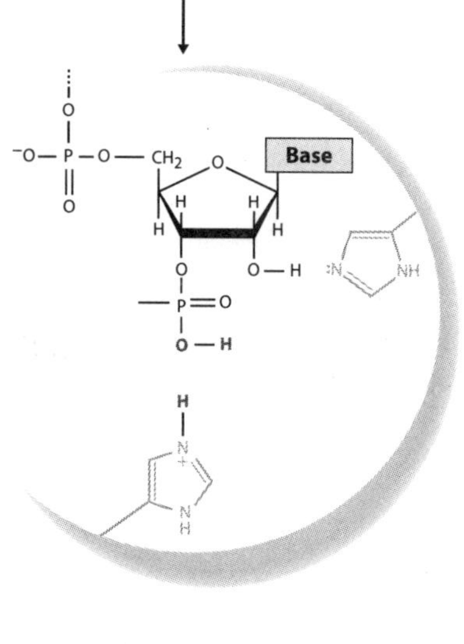

a. Draw a reaction coordinate diagram (energy versus reaction progress) with two curves, one depicting reaction 1 and the other depicting reaction 2. Be sure to label your curves and any important points on the curve.

b. At the molecular level, what does the enzyme do to speed up the reaction? Focus on molecular interactions that happen in the catalyzed versus uncatalyzed reactions. Any comments on energy must be linked to a discussion of molecular interactions.

c. Write an expression that reflects the change the enzyme makes in the thermodynamics of the catalyzed reaction compared to the uncatalyzed reaction. Explain why the expression you wrote speeds up a reaction.

Enzyme Kinetics

PRE-ACTIVITY ASSIGNMENT

1. Produce a reading log for the sections in your text that discuss the Michaelis-Menten equation, including k_{cat}.

2. Focus on the derivation of the Michaelis-Menten equation. List and explain the assumptions underlying the Michalis-Menten equation. Provide definitions for each term.

3. What is equal at equilibrium?

4. What is the general expression K_{eq} (the equilibrium constant) in terms of product and reactant concentration?

IN-CLASS ACTIVITY

Why

Enzymes catalyze most reactions that occur in biological systems and thus control the rates of these reactions. Examining the kinetics of an enzyme catalyzed reaction helps us learn about how enzymes function. In this activity, you will learn about the kinetic parameters that biochemists use to characterize enzymes and the graphical methods that allow biochemists to obtain kinetic parameters from experimental data.

Outcomes

1. Be able to articulate and apply what the enzyme parameters of K_M, V_{max}, k_{cat} and k_{cat}/K_M tell us about the enzyme.

2. Know the Michaelis-Menten rate equation and be able to utilize the rearranged versions of the Michaelis-Menten equation to determine the values for K_M and V_{max}.

3. Use K_M and V_{max} values to discuss qualities of enzymes related to their catalytic properties.

Plan

1. Form enzyme teams. Assign roles of manager, reflector, recorder, spokesperson.

2. Answer the Critical Thinking Questions.

3. Share two insights your team made about enzyme kinetics today.

Critical Thinking Questions

1. Recall your study of equilibria and kinetics from general chemistry. You used equations with upper case K and lower case k during the study of equilibria and kinetics respectively. What do the upper and lower case letters refer to?

   K = equilibrium constants
   k = rate constants

Equation 1
$$\frac{1}{V_o} = \frac{K_m}{V_{max}} \frac{1}{[S]} + \frac{1}{V_{max}}$$

Equation 2
$$E + S \underset{k_{-1}}{\overset{k_1}{\rightleftharpoons}} ES \overset{k_2}{\longrightarrow} E + P$$

Graph 1

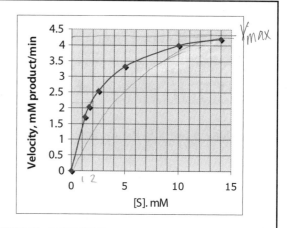

2. Compare your answers from your assignment and **take only two minutes**. Discuss the assumptions made during the derivation of the Michaelis-Menten equation. Be sure to consider assumptions pertaining to [ES], rate of product formation, [S], and number of substrates per reaction.

P→S can be ignored

[ES] is always constant → steady state

[S] is greater than [E]

3. Define the term V_{max} in your own words

The maximum rate that enzymes in a system can breakdown a substrate to products, assuming the enzyme is saturated

4. Solve the Michaelis-Menten equation for K_M when $V_o = V_{max}/2$. What does this tell you about the relationship between [substrate] and enzymes with high K_M values? With low K_M values? Make a generalization.

$V_0 = \frac{Vmax}{2}$

$Km = [S]$

$V_0 = \frac{Vmax [S]}{Km + [S]}$

$\frac{Vmax}{2} = \frac{Vmax \times [S]}{Km + [S]}$

$\frac{1}{2} = \frac{[S]}{Km + [S]}$

$\frac{1}{2}Km + \frac{1}{2}[S] = [S]$

$\frac{1}{2}Km = \frac{1}{2}[S]$

$\boxed{Km = [S]}$

Km = [S] where V_0 is $\frac{1}{2}$ Vmax
↑ Km needs ↑ [S]

5. a. What is the K_M value as you can estimate it from Graph 1?

Km ≈ 2

b. On Graph 1, draw a curve that has the same V_{max} but a larger K_M value.

6. Examine Equation 2. When k_2 is very small compared to k_{-1} the K_M becomes an approximation of the affinity of enzymes for substrate. Explain why this approximation makes sense. Does a large K_M indicate high or low affinity of enzyme for substrate?

large Km = low affinity. Because $km = \frac{k_2 + k_{-1}}{k_1}$ when k_2 is very small it becomes $km = \frac{k_{-1}}{k_1}$ (dissociation constant). This would then be about the E+S ⇌ ES so just the binding, not the breakdown → affinity

Foundations of Biochemistry

7. When k_2 is very small compared to k_1 and k_{-1}, what process is rate determining in product formation?

$$ES \rightarrow E + P$$

8. Many enzyme-catalyzed processes are multi-step reactions.
   a. In a multi-step reaction, what step determines the overall reaction rate?

   The slowest step

   b. What step in M-M kinetics determines overall reaction rate?

   $$ES \xrightarrow{k_2} E + P \qquad Kcat$$

   c. The term used for the overall rate constant for multi-stp reactions is k_{cat}. Discuss why it makes sense that $k_{cat} = k_2$ in simple Michaelis-Menten reactions.

   Because [ES] is constant so we can ignore $E + S \underset{k_{-1}}{\overset{k_1}{\rightleftharpoons}} ES$

   So the part that limits is $ES \xrightarrow{k_2} E + P$ and therefore

   we look at k_2 which equals $Kcat$

   $\quad$ Kcat has to be as slow as the slowest step.

9. In simple M-M kinetics, the units of k_{cat} are s^{-1}. Discuss how the units are consistent with the name "turnover number." If k_{cat} is large, what does that imply about the enzyme?

   turnover # = # substrate converted per unit of time, so s^{-1} makes perfect sense as a unit.

   $Kcat = \uparrow$ then the enzyme is more efficient
   $\qquad \qquad \qquad \hookrightarrow$ more product per unit time

10. The term *efficiency* is often used in describing enzymes. What does it mean for an enzyme to be efficient?

   To break down substrates at a quick rate but also to work better at low [S] $\hookrightarrow$ per unit of time

continued on next page

11. How is your answer to question 9 consistent with the term for catalytic efficiency (k_{cat}/K_m)? Discuss the contribution of the terms k_{cat} and K_M to the overall term of catalytic efficiency.

$$\frac{K_{cat} \uparrow}{Km \downarrow}$$ gives the highest affinity, and catalytic efficiency

what M-M is all about!

12. Discuss the meaning of enzyme reaction mechanism in the context of catalysis. How does the study of enzyme kinetics relate to reaction mechanism?

Consider the enzymes in the table below and answer the following questions. Answers should be brief (1-3 sentences).

Enzyme	$K_M(M)$	$k_{cat}(s^{-1})$
A	9.5×10^{-5}	1.4×10^4
B	2.5×10^{-2}	1.0×10^7
C	5.0×10^{-6}	8.0×10^2

$\frac{K_{cat}}{Km}$

1.4737×10⁸   1.47×10⁸
400,000,000   4.0×10⁸
160,00,000   1.6×10⁷

1. Which enzyme has the highest affinity for substrate? How do you know?

2. Which enzyme converts the most substrate to product in a given period of time? How do you know?

Method of initial rate

3. Which enzyme has the highest catalytic efficiency? How do you know?

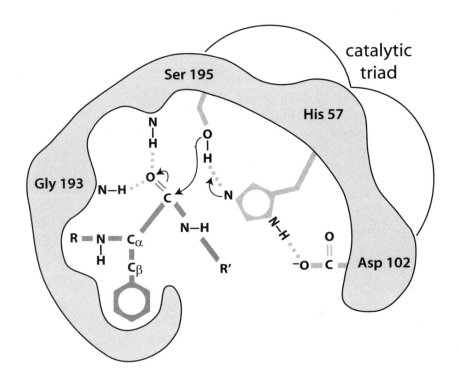

Ser 195

catalytic triad

His 57

Gly 193

N–H

R—N—C$_\alpha$

H

C$_\beta$

N–H

R'

N–H

O

–O—C

Asp 102

A diagram of the enzyme active site for chymotrypsin is shown. The amino acids Gly 193, Ser 195, His 57 and Asp 102 form part of the active site. The amino acids Ser 195, His 57 and Asp 102 comprise what is known as the catalytic triad. A portion of a natural peptide substrate from R to R' is depicted with the residue phenylalanine occupying the hydrophobic pocket of the enzyme.

4. Chymotrypsin is a serine protease enzyme. The K_M for the reaction of chymotrypsin with N-acetylvaline ethyl ester is 8.8×10^{-2} M, and the K_M for the reaction of chymotrypsin with N-acetyltyrosine ethyl ester is 6.6×10^{-4} M.

$Km = 8.8 \times 10^{-2}$

$Km = 6.6 \times 10^{-4}$

a. Which substrate has a higher apparent affinity for the enzyme?

b. Propose a reason for the difference in affinity based on the shape of each of the substrates (see active site figure, chymotrypsin cleaves on the C-side of aromatic residues).

c. Which of the substrates is likely to have a higher V_{max}?

(This page intentionally left blank.)

Enzyme Inhibition

1. Read over the sections in your book about enzyme inhibition.

2. Write a brief statement explaining why scientists conduct inhibition studies. What knowledge do we gain from them?

3. Answer Critical Thinking Questions 2 and 3 in the Activity using the data from Model 1 only.

4. You should bring a calculator to class.

Why

Data from studies of enzyme inhibition are used to determine K_M^{app} and V_{max}^{app}. A comparison of these values are with the K_M and V_{max} values observed when only substrate is present is used to understand the nature of the inhibition. A large number of pharmaceutical drugs on the market are enzyme inhibitors. In addition, competitive inhibitors are particularly useful to suggest features of the active site.

Outcomes

1. Interpret graphical representations of the Michaelis-Menten rate equation to characterize the nature of the inhibition.

2. Use graphical representations to determine the values for K_M, V_{max}, and K_I.

3. Describe the unique chemical environment (geometry and proximity) of the catalytic active site and discuss its effect on reaction rate.

Plan

1. Form groups and assign roles of manager, recorder, spokesperson/skeptic, and reflector.

2. Complete Critical Thinking Question which follow. For questions 1 and 2, quickly compare individual answers from assignment. Prepare your spokesperson to share answers.

3. Reflect on your group's ability to process the graphical information presented in this activity. What did you do well? What changes could you make to help you better process information presented in graphs in the future?

Model 1   Idealized Graphs of Enzyme Inhibition

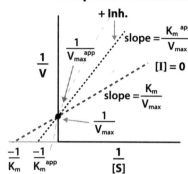
Competitive Inhibition

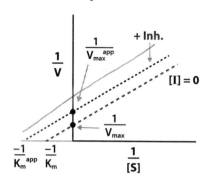
Uncompetitive Inhibition

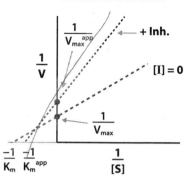
Mixed Inhibition

Critical Thinking Questions

1. Compare individual answers to questions 2 and 3 completed as part of the assignment.

2. How does the value of V_{max} for the enzyme compare to the V_{max}^{app} of the inhibited enzyme for:

   a. A competitive inhibitor

   > Same

   b. An uncompetitive inhibitor

   > ↑ Vmax

   c. Mixed inhibition

   > ↑ Vmax^app

3. How does the value of K_M for the enzyme compare to the K_M^{app} of the inhibited enzyme for:

   a. A competitive inhibitor

   > ↑ app

   b. An uncompetitive inhibitor

   > ↓ app

   c. Mixed inhibition

   > ↑ app

4. For each situation in Model 1, consider an inhibitor that is better than the one shown on graph. Answer the following questions for each type of inhibition:

   a. How would K_M^{app} change?

   > higher, decreased, higher

   b. How would V_{max}^{app} change?

   > same, lower, lower

   c. Draw a line on the graphs that would represent the new, better inhibitor.

Foundations of Biochemistry

Model 2   Real Data of Enzyme Inhibition

[S] (mmol/L)	Velocity [(mmol/L)min⁻¹]			
	No inhibitor	Inhibitor A	Inhibitor B 3mM	Inhibitor B 5mM
1.25	1.72	0.98	1.25	1.01
1.67	2.04	1.17	1.54	1.26
2.50	2.63	1.47	2.00	1.72
5.00	3.33	1.96	2.86	2.56
10.00	4.17	2.38	3.70	3.49

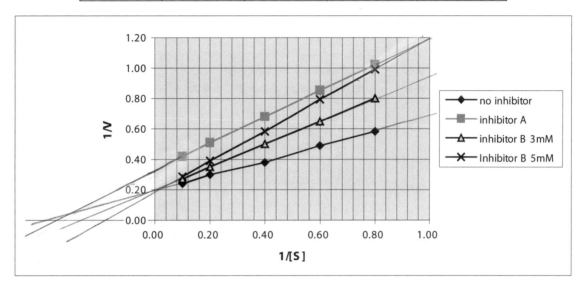

5. To make meaningful interpretations of data from double-reciprocal plots, the lines need to extend through the y-axis to the x-axis. Draw those extensions on the graph. Label the x- and y-intercepts with the appropriate terms, V_{max}, K_M, V_{max}^{app}, K_M^{app}. The label could be negative or inverse of the terms listed.

6. Using the equations given below, calculate the values of V_{max}, K_M, V_{max}^{app}, and K_M^{app} for each line shown in Model 2. Have each group member be responsible for one line. Compare answers and complete the table.

		V_{max}	K_M	V_{max}^{app}	K_M^{app}
No inhibitor	y = 0.4843x + 0.1951	5.1256	2.4823		
Inhibitor A	y = 0.8582x + 0.3369			2.9682	2.5473
Inhibitor B 3mM	y = 0.755x + 0.1969			5.0787	3.8344
Inhibitor B 5mM	y = 1.006x + 0.1861			5.3735	5.4057

7. Predict the type of inhibition for each inhibitor in Model 2.

B → competitive → Vmax is same
A-mixed   Km is same

continued on next page

↓Km ↑affinity
↓Km^app
lower potency = doesn't bind as well

8. What does a large K_I value for a competitive inhibitor indicate about the potency of the inhibition? Note that the equation that relates K_I to values from the graphs is shown below.

$$K_M^{app} = K_M\left(1+\frac{[I]}{K_I}\right)$$

lowered inhibition potency because smaller Km means higher affinity for substrate

9. Chymotrypsin is a serine protease enzyme that continues to be widely studied to examine structure–activity relationships. The physiological substrates are proteins, but many non-physiological substrates are used to simplify the activity assay. One such substrate is ethyl N-acetyl-L-tyrosinate (structure below).

$K_I = 1.96 \times 10^{-4}\,M$ $K_I = 1.0 \times 10^{-2}\,M$

ethyl N-acetyl-L-tyrosinate   benzeneboronic acid   benzylalcohol

Inhibition studies were conducted with the two competitive inhibitors, benzeneboronic acid and benzylalcohol, and the K_I values determined. [M. Philipp and M. L. Bender, (1971) *Proc. of the Natl. Acad. of Sci.* **68** pp478-480.]

a. Which inhibitor binds with the greatest affinity?

   benzeneboronic acid

b. Propose an explanation for the difference in affinity based on the structure and shape of the two inhibitors.

   Can form more interactions with the enzyme because of the extra OH. More polar parts to react.

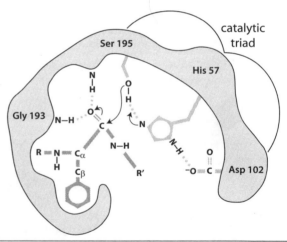

A diagram of the enzyme active site for chymotrypsin is shown. The amino acids Gly 193, Ser 195, His 57 and Asp 102 form part of the active site. A portion of a natural peptide substrate from R to R' is depicted with the residue phenylalanine occupying the hydrophobic pocket of the enzyme.

c. Propose another competitive inhibitor to test and predict whether it would have a higher or lower K_I value. Refer to specific interactions that this proposed inhibitor may have with the active site (see diagram of chymotrypsin active site).

1. The kinetic data at right were obtained for an enzyme in the absence of inhibitor (trial A), and in the presence of two different inhibitors (B and C) at concentrations of 5 mM.

[S] (mM)	A no inhibitor V (µmole/sec)	B V (µmole/sec)	C V (µmole/sec)
1	12	4.3	5.5
2	20	8	9
4	29	14	13
8	35	21	16
12	40	26	18

a. Determine V_{max} and K_M for the enzyme (Assume $[E_T]$ is the same for each trial.) If you determine these values via a graphing calculator you need to so state and draw a small graph to show the data. If you use an actual graph to determine these values, it needs to be at least 5 inches × 5 inches.

b. Determine the type of inhibition and provide a reason why you chose what you did. Determine the K_I for any competitive inhibitors.

c. Comment on the possible structural similarities between the substrate and the two inhibitors.

(This page intentionally left blank.)

Foundations of Biochemistry

IN-CLASS ~~ACTIVITY~~

Why

Over the past few class periods you have learned about enzyme catalysis, kinetics and inhibition. Today is your opportunity to solidify your understanding, practice what you have learned, and ask questions.

Outcomes

1. Describe the unique chemical environment (geometry and proximity) of the catalytic active site and discuss its effect on reaction rate.

2. Gain confidence in your ability to solve problems related to enzyme kinetics and catalysis.

Plan

1. Form groups and assign roles of manager, recorder, spokesperson/skeptic, and reflector.

2. Complete the following problems. Prepare your spokesperson to share answers.

3. Identify the two most important things your group learned about problem solving today that will help you solve new problems.

4. Identify features of this problem and its solution that could apply to other problems.

Critical Thinking Questions

1. Studies (kinetic, stereochemical, chemical modification and site specific mutagenesis experiments) on the enzyme triosephosphate isomerase have identified the base "B" as Glu[165] and the acid "HA" as His[95] J. R. Knowles, *Nature* **350**, 121 (1991). To aid your understanding, draw the active site as a pocket that extends into the enzyme and place the Glu and His on opposite sides of the pocket.

   a. Drawing of the pocket:

   b. How might the replacement of Glu with Asp affect the catalytic rate?

   c. Discuss what form His would be in at a physiological pH of 7.2. Would that pH allow it to act as a general acid? Describe the conditions that allow it to act as a general acid. (Hint: What reaction does a K_a refer to?) Can you reconcile this apparent contradiction?   *b acts as an acid... why?*

continued on next page

d. Discuss the implications of these structural issues in terms of the effectiveness of the active site.

2. Pyroglutaryl-peptidase II, PPII, is an ectopeptidase (enzyme) that serves an important role in the regulation of the biologically active thyrotropin-releasing hormone, TRH. It acts by cleaving the terminal pyroglutamic acid (Glp) from TRH, [Glp-His-ProNH$_2$, pyroglutamyl-histidyl-prolineamide]. The enzyme does not cleave any other peptides that contain a terminal Glp residue, thereby displaying significant substrate specificity toward TRH with a K_M value of 35µM. Since the action of TRH in the central nervous system (CNS) can be beneficial for treatment of certain CNS disorders, such as epilepsy and memory loss, selective inhibition of PPII could serve to modulate the active levels of TRH. To date there is no experimental structure for PPII on which to base the rational design of active site directed inhibitors. Therefore a series of competitive inhibitors have been designed and tested. Some of that data is shown below, however they analyzed more than 50 compounds in their study (adapted from *Biochemical Journal* **389** (2006) pp569-576).

$K_m = 35 \mu M$

pyroglutamyl-histidyl-prolineamide   pyroglutamyl-asparaginyl-prolineamide   pyroglutamic acid

#	Name	Asn derivatives	K_I, µM
1	Glp-His-ProNH$_2$	none	Normal substrate, no K_I
2	Glp-Asn-ProNH$_2$	none	17.5
	Glp-Asn(derivatives)-ProNH$_2$	Asn amide H replaced with	
3		methyl	103
4		methyl and methyl (both H replaced)	>200

we know competitive

a. Sketch a graph of $1/V°$ versus $1/[S]$ for the four different compounds (using 1-4). Label the relevant points on your sketch that are expected given the information provided about the compounds.

b. Compare compounds 2, 3 and 4 with the normal substrate and draw conclusions about the active site.

$Km^{app} = Km\left(1 + \frac{[I]}{K_I}\right)$

Section 11

Carbohydrates and Glycoproteins

PRE-ACTIVITY ASSIGNMENT

1. Prepare a reading outline for the section in your book that covers general carbohydrate and glycoprotein structure. Be sure you review the alpha (α) and beta (β) anomers of sugar.

2. Make copies of the 3D structures of cellulose and of amylose from your textbook (or online if needed) and bring to class. Do not bring sketches.

3. Some carbohydrates are metabolized for energy, whereas others are structural molecules. Identify three of each from the reading.

4. Biochemists often refer to the major classes of biological macromolecules as proteins, nucleic acids, carbohydrates, and lipids. List and explain three ways in which proteins and carbohydrates are different as classes of molecules. List three ways in which they are similar.

5. If time permits, watch the movie, "Inner Life of the Cell."

IN-CLASS ACTIVITY

Why

Although carbohydrates are typically thought of as energy sources, they also serve an important role as structural molecules and modifiers of protein structure and function.

Outcomes

1. Recognize and describe the structural and functional diversity of carbohydrates.

2. Describe how carbohydrates interact with proteins and explain the consequences of these interactions.

3. Develop the abilities to identify and use diverse backgrounds of group members to solve interdisciplinary problems.

Plan

1. Form macromolecules teams. Assign roles of manager, spokesperson, recorder, and reflector.

2. The person whose hometown is the most distant from here assumes the role of manager. The manager should assign remaining roles.

3. Answer the Critical Thinking Questions.

4. This activity requires some specific biology knowledge. Identify group members with prior biology coursework and make a plan to ensure their participation.

Critical Thinking Questions

1. Compare answers on Question 4 of the assignment. Make one generalization about carbohydrates as a class of molecules.

   Carbohydrates can be used for energy or structure => that is their function.

2. Discuss whether the two forms of glucose shown in the figure below would be equally likely to be the substrate for a given enzyme. Would α-D-glucopyranose and α-D-fructofuranose be equally likely to be the substrate for a given enzyme? Refer to both shape and noncovalent interactions in your answer. Make one generalization about protein-carbohydrate interactions.

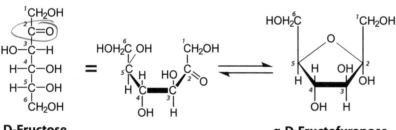

D-Glucose

α-D-Glucopyranose (Haworth projection)

D-Fructose

α-D-Fructofuranose (Haworth projection)

   No, because of the difference in location of the carbonyl the shape will be different for each. The weak interactions will also be placed in different locations.

3. Use the structures of cellulose and amylose you brought to class. What is the same about the two figures? What is different? What stabilizes these structures?

   One more hydroxyl on cellulose residues, amylose has a CH₂OH group where cellulose has an OH group. Cellulose is β linked, amylose is α linked. Their overall structure is very similar
   amylose → helical   cellulose → sheets

4. What allows for the variety of complex structures seen in carbohydrates? Are carbohydrates more or less structurally versatile than amino acids? How could structural diversity make carbohydrates ideal for intercellular communication?

   More structurally versatile than amino acids. The stereochemistry allows for variety → chiral centers. Each signal can be more specific => allowing for more communication

5. When glycoproteins are synthesized in the cell, at what stage of the polymerization of the protein are the sugar groups added: Prior to translation, cotranslationally, or posttranslationally?

posttranslationally

Information

Glycoproteins are an important class of proteins. There are many families of glycoproteins: lectins and selectins are examples. All lectins have a pattern of invariant and highly conserved amino acid residues forming the carbohydrate-recognition domain (CRD). As the name CRD implies lectins can bind carbohydrates in a specific manner. The majority of C-type lectins are large asymmetric transmembrane glycoproteins. Selectins are similar to lectins. The selectin family of adhesion molecules mediates the initial attachment of leukocytes (white blood cells) to vascular endothelial cells before their firm adhesion and movement into tissues at sites of tissue injury and inflammation.

6. Draw a picture of a cell with a transmembrane lectin.

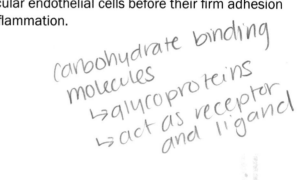

carbohydrate binding molecules
↳ glycoproteins
↳ act as receptor and ligand

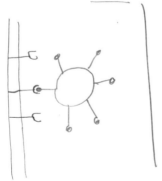

7. Draw a picture of a cell with a selectin interacting with the vascular endothelium.

8. Therapeutic agents are currently being investigated that block the action of selectins in order to prevent the pathological effects resulting from leukocyte entry into sites of inflammation. These agents are molecules that inhibit the selectin. Describe molecules that might be effective.

Something with similar shape/structure/charge as the ligand that naturally binds
competitive inhibitor but to binding site not active site

9. Review your plan.

1. CEL-I is a C-type lectin, purified from the sea cucumber *Cucumaria echinata*, that shows a high specificity for *N*-acetylgalactosamine (GalNAc). Lectins are proteins that interact with carbohydrates. An X-ray crystallographic image of GalNAc interacting with specific amino acids of CEL-I is shown below (Sugawara, H. et al. J. Biol. Chem. 2004;279:45219-45225, used by permission). [NOTE: Two different X-ray crystallographic images showing slightly different configurations are overlaid in the image below.]

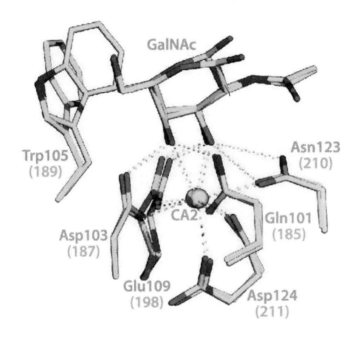

a. Draw the molecular structure of GalNAc (your textbook may have a picture of GalNAc or of GlcNAc which has a glucose instead of galactose).

b. List the noncovalent interactions that occur to stabilize the interaction of GalNAc with the protein. Name the amino acid or ion involved in each interaction. The sphere CA2 is a coordinated calcium ion.

c. Explain how changing Trp105 to alanine would affect the ability of CEL-I to interact with GalNAc. What about changing Asp124 to alanine?

Lipid Structure and Function

1. Produce a reading outline for the section that discusses the major classes of lipids and some of their unique structures including micelles and bilayers.

2. Give a brief definition of each of the 5 major classes of lipids, (fatty acids, triacylglycerols, glycerophospho-lipids, sphingolipids and steroids). Draw one example molecule for each.

IN-CLASS ACTIVITY

Why

Lipids are a class of biological compounds characterized by the fact that they are soluble in organic solvents. Thus, compared to other classes of biological compounds, a variety of different structural classes are represented. Not unexpectedly, the functions that lipids perform are also quite diverse.

Outcomes

1. Review and be able to use the vocabulary pertaining to lipid structure.

2. Assign a potential biological function to a given lipid structure and shape.

3. Describe the connection between lipid structure and function, paying particular attention to membrane fluidity.

4. Generalize the behavior of lipids in aqueous environments to include the behavior of other hydrophobic molecules in aqueous environments.

Plan

1. Assign roles. Answer Critical Thinking Questions.

2. Prepare questions that you need answered concerning lipid structure and function.

3. Cite two examples of how you carried out your group role today and share these with your group.

Critical Thinking Questions

1. a. Refer to the 5 classes of lipids you defined in your assignment and the structures found in your text. Identify each as polar, nonpolar, or amphiphilic.

   b. If lipids can be polar nonpolar and amphiphilic, what characteristic is the defining feature for lipids?

2. How is the definition of "lipid" similar to and different from the types of definitions used for other bio-molecules such as proteins and carbohydrates?

3. Write representative structures for a fatty acid in the *cis* and the *trans* configuration and number the carbons.

4. The melting points of oleic acid, C18:1 Δ9*cis*, versus elaidic acid, C18:1 Δ9*trans*, are 16.3 °C and 44.8 °C respectively. What do the data imply about the two fatty acids?

pg 374
↳all three lipid aggregates

Model 1

Stylized Structure	Packing Shape	Examples
O— polar group ~~~~ nonpolar tail	cone-like	fatty acids lysophophatides detergents
O— polar group ~~~~ nonpolar tails	cylinder-like	glycerophospholipids sphingolipids

Model 2   Lipid Aggregates in Water

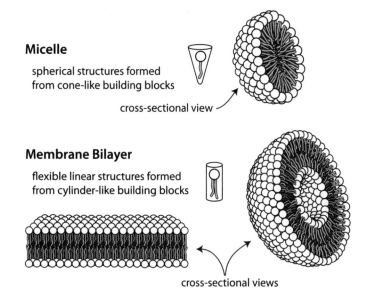

Micelle

spherical structures formed
from cone-like building blocks

cross-sectional view

Membrane Bilayer

flexible linear structures formed
from cylinder-like building blocks

cross-sectional views

5. Refer to Models 1 and 2.

   a. What shape and structural factors determine the sort of lipid aggregate that will form in an aqueous environment?

   b. Identify a specific molecule that could fit the shape and structural parameters outlined in the model for forming a micelle.

   c. Do the same for the shape and structural parameters outlined in the model for a membrane bilayer.

6. Partially hydrogenated vegetable oils (triacylglycerols) contain *trans* double bonds instead of the naturally occurring *cis* double bonds. Explain how the substitution of the *cis* double bond by a *trans* double bond in the fatty acid of a membrane phospholipid might affect the membrane characteristics.

continued on next page

7. Cell membranes are self-sealing; that is, if they are punctured or disrupted mechanically, they quickly and spontaneously reseal. What properties of membrane components are responsible for this feature? Compare the self-sealing of membranes to the process of protein folding.

8. What feature of membranes help explain why lipid flip-flop is very rare?

9. Locate the structure for cholesterol. How is it structurally similar to other membrane lipids? How is it different? Based on the figure below, suggest a function for cholesterol in biological membranes.

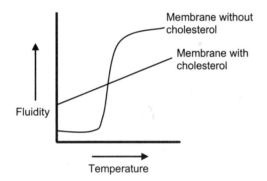

POST-ACTIVITY SKILL EXERCISES

1. Triacylglycerols are not found in lipid bilayers, why not?

2. Snake venom contains the enzyme phospholipase A_2. The action of phospholipase A_2 cleaves the fatty acid tail from the position 2 of a phospholipid structure. Select a phospholipid, and use it to illustrate the action of phospholipase A_2 and discuss the structural ramifications of this reaction on the membrane.

Membranes and Transmembrane Proteins

1. Produce a reading outline for the section in your textbook that discusses membrane proteins including ✓ lipid rafts.

2. Define the terms *peripheral membrane protein* and *integral membrane protein*.

3. Transport and receptor activity are two of the most important functions of integral membrane proteins. For these two functions, describe the features of primary, secondary and tertiary protein structure that allows proteins to perform these functions.

Why

Membranes are some of the most important macrostructures of biological systems. Membranes define the organism and separate it from its environment. All biological membranes contain lipids as major components. Understanding how these lipids contribute to the structure of membranes and interact with membrane proteins will help you understand the important functions the membrane carries out.

Outcomes

1. Describe the general structural characteristics of membrane lipids and how these characteristics are important for the construction of membranes.

2. Describe the types of interactions that occur between membrane lipids and membrane proteins and use that to make predictions about the structure of proteins in membranes.

3. Improve your ability to communicate answers to questions clearly and concisely.

Plan

1. Form teams. Assign roles.

2. Answer Critical Thinking Questions.

3. Create a list of structural characteristics that could be used to identify membrane lipids and proteins.

4. As a group, review answers to Critical Thinking Questions and work with the spokesperson to craft clear and concise responses.

Critical Thinking Questions

1. The relative orientation of polar and nonpolar amino acid side chains of integral membrane proteins is "inside-out" compared to the amino acid side chain orientation for globular water-soluble proteins. Explain why.

Information

Integral membrane proteins often contain helical segments of appropriate length to span the lipid bilayer. In a protein that has a single segment that spans the membrane, the helix usually only contains hydrophobic residues and is called a single-span membrane protein. In transmembrane proteins with multiple segments that span the membrane, hydrophilic residues are often found in sequences of the helices.

2. Why are hydrophobic residues favored in single-span membrane proteins? Find an example of a single-span membrane protein in your book.

3. Propose a structural orientation and a function for multiple hydrophilic residues in the helices of a multi-span protein. Find an example of a multi-span membrane protein in your book.

4. Why are hydrophobic interactions NOT a factor in the association of lipid-linked (peripheral) proteins with membranes?

5. From your understanding of protein structure and membrane structure, explain the fact that of the approximately 51,000 protein structures (3D) published and listed in the Protein Data Bank (in 2008) only about 930 of these structures are transmembrane proteins. NOTE: 3D structures are typically obtained from X-ray crystallography data.

6. Allergies are the result of an overactive immune system. The immune system responds to a variety of allergens; these can be inhaled, contact or ingested allergens. The symptoms resulting from these allergens are caused by the release of histamine, structure shown below.

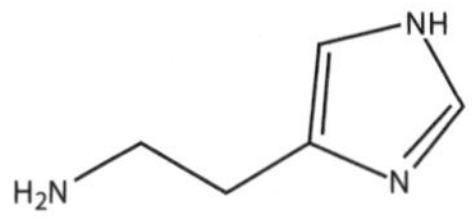

histamine

Histamine acts by binding to specialized membrane proteins called histamine H1 receptors. These receptors, found in specific cells, are integral membrane proteins that possess seven transmembrane α-helical regions. The amino terminus of the protein is extracellular, while the C-terminus is cytoplasmic. The binding of histamine to the extracellular portion of the H1 receptor prompts a conformational change in the intracellular C-terminus region of the protein. This conformational change triggers numerous intracellualar signaling events that stimulate the immune response in cells containing the receptor.

There are numerous anti-histamine drugs available commercially. Some of the most popular are shown below.

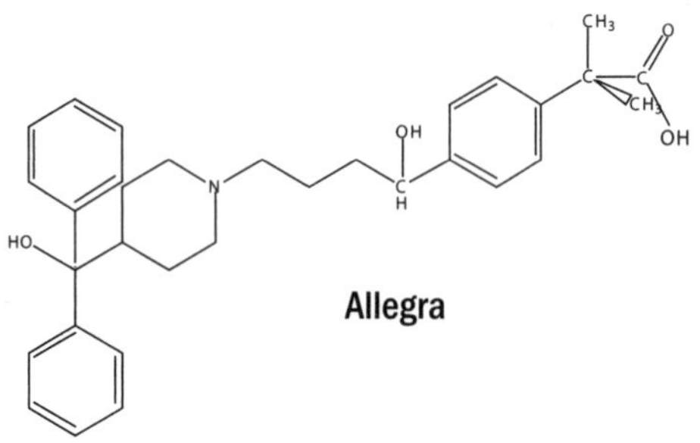

Allegra

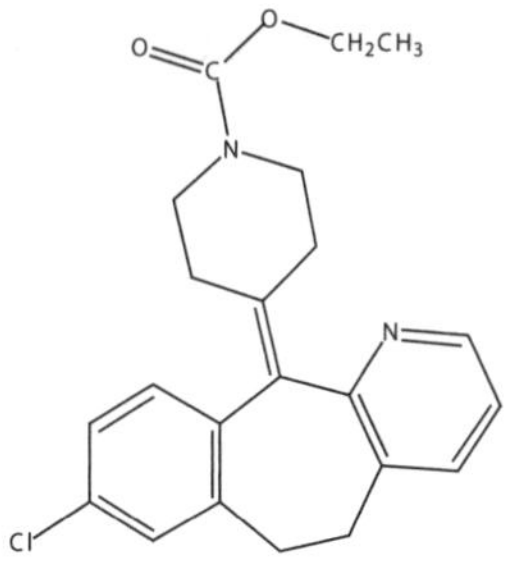

Claritan

Propose a reasonable mode of action by which these antihistamines exert their activity.

7. Cell membranes are described using a fluid mosaic model, yet they are also discussed as containing microdomains (lipid rafts). Define the fluid mosaic model. Does this model fully describe the reality of a cell membrane? Explain why or why not. Describe lipid rafts and suggest two possible functions.

span insulin receptor → Integral   Glucophorin → carries sugar molecules
bacteriorhodopsin → crosses bilayer 7 times, light-driven proton pump → signal reception
succinate dehydrogenase → integral protein → participates in CAC and ETC

POST-ACTIVITY SKILL EXERCISES

1. Why is it important for determining the function of a membrane protein to know if it spans the bilayer or appears only on one face of the membrane? As part of your answer give three example proteins and their functions.

Integral membrane proteins: firmly associated w/ lipid bilayer, removable only by agents that interfere w/ hydrophobic interactions

Peripheral membrane proteins: associate w/ membrane through electrostatic interactions + h-bonding

Amphitropic proteins: found in both the cytosol + membranes

• Specific orientation in bilayer ⇒ sidedness

2. The protein OmpF porin is embedded in the cell membrane and serves as a pore through the membrane. Structural analysis of the protein shown that the outside of the protein has a band of hydrophobic residues that is 27Å tall and interacts directly with the nonpolar membrane (Penel et al *Biochime* 1998; 80; 543-51). The upper and lower bounds of the band are defined by phenylalanine residues. The following shape represents a side view of the protein that is 40Å tall. Draw the lipid bilayer on the shape below and indicate the location of the phenylalanine residues.

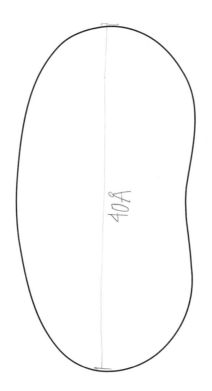

40Å

Section 14

Membrane Proteins — Interpreting a Research Paper

IN-CLASS **ACTIVITY**

"In Vitro Synthesis of Lactose Permease to Probe the Mechanism of Membrane Insertion and Folding", Shushi Nagamori, et al., *Journal of Biological Chemistry* Vol 278, pp. 14820-14826, 2003. The article can be downloaded for free in PDF format from www.jbc.org

Assignment: Read and analyze Nagamori, et. al., 2003. As you read, make a list of all words you don't know so you can begin defining them. After reading, produce a statement of what, specifically, each figure is investigating. Briefly state the results of each experiment and the authors' interpretation of the results. Bring any questions you have about the methodology and the experiments to class. We will be analyzing the remainder of the paper in an activity in class.

Each group will have a part of the research paper to present. To give you more time to prepare, assignments for each group are listed below. Also attached is a table to help you consider key elements of each section of the paper. Prepare individually or as a group as you see fit. As you analyze your section of the paper, keep the following in mind. The authors' overriding goal is to establish an *in vitro* model to study protein insertion into membranes. Much is known about the topology (orientation and interactions of protein helices in the membrane) of LacY *in vivo*. The immediate goal of this paper is to gather information about the topology of LacY in their *in vitro* system. If the topology *in vitro* is similar to *in vivo*, the authors will be able to use this system to study the details of protein insertion into the membrane. The discussion section of the paper does a good job of summarizing results and putting them into context.

Introduction I & II:

Figure 1:

Figure 2

Figure 3B:

Figure 3A:

Figure 4:

Figure 5:

Figure 6:

Figure 7:

Conclusions:

65

Introduction I	• Focus on first two paragraphs of intro only (up to citation 30) • What organism is being studied? • What is the general area of interest? • What are the unanswered questions in the area of membrane protein insertion? • What particular protein is being studied? What is its function? What is the structure of the protein? Use the structural diagram provided.
Introduction II	• Focus on last two paragraphs of intro and Fig 3B • When are proteins inserted into the membrane? • What is PE? What is its role in membrane insertion? • What structural elements of LacY are needed for proper membrane insertion? • What is the significance of a membrane protein being resistant to proteolysis?
Fig1	• What are ISO vesicles? What are RSO vesicles? • What size would you expect LacY to be on a gel? • What is the significance of seeing LacY in the pellet? • What do the urea/alkaline treatment do? • What are the conclusions from Fig 1?
Fig 2	• What are factor Xa protease sites? • Where is loop VI/VII? Where is loop VII/VIII? • Are these loops facing the inside or outside of an ISO vesicle? • What is DDM? • What is the significance of proteoloysis in 2A? • What does antibody 4B11 bind to? • What is the difference between in vitro and in vivo? • What is the conclusion from Fig 2?
Fig 3B	• What is TDG? • What is the significance of NEM binding in Fig 3? • What is the conclusion for Fig 3B?

Fig 3A	• What technique is being used? • What is being measured and why? • What is Dns6-gal? • Why is lactose sometimes added to medium? • What is the conclusion from figure 3A?
Fig 4	• What is N6? What is known about its expression *in vitro*? • What is the significance of seeing a band in ppt vs. sup? • What is puromycin? — *translation inhibitor* • What are 226 and 312? →*amino acid attached to* • What is the conclusion from Fig 4?
Fig 5	• Where is loop IV/V? • What does susceptibility to Xa protease say about insertion into membrane? • What is the role of ribosome attachment in protein folding? • What is the conclusion from Fig 5?
Fig 6	• What mutants are being examined? What is role of the mutated residues? • What is the role of DTT in these experiments? • What is being crosslinked, and what does crosslinking suggest about protein folding? • What is the conclusion from Fig 6?
Fig 7	• What is FtsH? • What is a temperature sensitive mutant? • What is the conclusion from Fig 7?
Conclusions	• Summarize major conclusions from figures • What was the authors' goal? Did they accomplish it? • How will these data be used as a foundation for future experiments?

Handwritten annotations: N-terminus → 6 transmembrane helices → not expressed

hydrophobic region : 27 Å

About 18 residues

1) Ser
2) Ala
3) Leu
4) Val
polar — 5) Thr
6) Iso
7) Ala
8) Leu
polar — 9) Asp
10) Ala
11) Leu
polar — 12) Gln
KINK 13) Pro
14)
15)
16)
17)
18)

Transmembrane Proteins Problem

IN-CLASS ACTIVITY

The structure of the *E. coli* lactose permease LacY as determined by X-ray crystallography is given below (Abramson et al, *Science* 301, 610-615, 2003; used by permission). Using the information given in the figure and your knowledge of protein structure, propose an amino acid sequence for <u>helix V</u> and justify your choices. Suggest roles for the amino acids identified in the helix schematic and explain your choices for the remaining amino acids. Be specific and use your chemistry. Before presenting your group answer to the class, consider whether it makes sense. What criteria would you use to determine whether your proposed sequence makes sense?

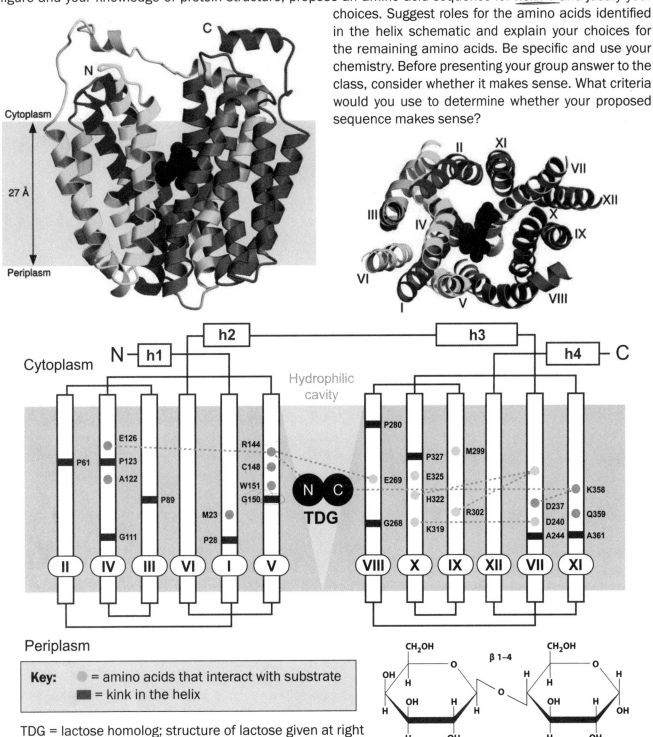

Key: ● = amino acids that interact with substrate
■ = kink in the helix

TDG = lactose homolog; structure of lactose given at right

(This page intentionally left blank.)

Problem Solving

IN-CLASS ACTIVITY

1. As we have seen previously, ribonuclease (RNase) can be completely denatured by heating or with chemical denaturants (urea, 2-mercaptoethanol) yet can refold to its fully active form on cooling or removal of the denaturants. If trypsin and α-chymotrypsin are denatured, however, they do not regain activity following cooling or denaturant removal even though they are not significantly different in size from RNase. **Explain, in structural terms, why the structures of trypsin and α-chymotrypsin would preclude their renaturation to fully active forms.**

2. Carbon monoxide is toxic to humans and animals because it binds very tightly to the O_2 binding sites on myoglobin (Mb) and hemoglobin (Hb), acting as a competitive inhibitor of O_2. Dangerous levels of CO are generated by car exhaust, industry, faulty stoves, furnaces, etc. We can write the set of binding equilibria for Mb as follows:

$$Mb + O_2 + CO \underset{\substack{\uparrow\downarrow \ p_{50}^{CO}}}{\overset{p_{50}^{O_2}}{\rightleftharpoons}} MbO_2$$

$$MbCO$$

The $\boldsymbol{p_{50}}^{O_2}$ is an equilibrium constant for the dissociation of MbO_2 as is p_{50}^{CO} for MbCO.

a. Write the reaction for the dissociation of MbO_2.

b. What are two other important equilibrium constants (that we have discussed) that are dissociation constants?

    Use these values to answer the questions below.

    $\boldsymbol{p_{50}}^{O_2} = 0.4$ kPa $\boldsymbol{p_{50}}^{CO} = .001$ kPa pO_2 (sea level) = 12 kPa

c. The expression for Y_{CO}, the fractional saturation of Mb sites is:

$$Y_{CO} = \frac{pCO}{p_{50}^{CO} + pCO}$$

    Clean air contains very low amounts of CO, with $\boldsymbol{p}CO = .001$ kPa. What fraction of Mb is in the MbCO form for this level of CO, assuming there is <u>NO</u> oxygen present?

d. Complete the same calculation for MbO_2 with <u>NO</u> carbon monoxide present, where $\boldsymbol{p}O_2 = 12$ kPa.

continued on next page

e. The expression for the fractional saturation of Mb with CO in the presence of O_2 can be written as $Y_{CO} = pCO/(\alpha \, p_{50}co + pCO)$. The term "$\alpha$" is completely analogous to the one used for competitive inhibitors in the Michaelis-Menten equation $K_M^{app} = \alpha K_M$.

Calculate the fraction of Mb in the MbCO form in clean air, where $pO_2 = 12$ kPa. In this case the O_2 is functioning as the "inhibitor." The equation for "α" is shown below:

$$\alpha = 1 + \frac{[I]}{K_I}$$

f. Carbon monoxide poisoning occurs when CO in the air reaches dangerous levels. Death occurs when the saturation of Mb with CO is 80%. What pCO does this level correspond to, assuming the partial pressure of O_2 remains at 12 kPa (as above)?

3. Identify the most important thing you learned about problem solving today that will help you solve new problems.

DNA and the Central Dogma

No preactivity assignment is necessary, but some prior foundational biology knowledge is expected.

Why

Nucleic acids are large molecules with three-dimensional structures that are more predictable than those of proteins. DNA and RNA are composed of a small set of monomeric building blocks. DNA serves as the repository for all of the genetic information of an organism. How DNA is used by the organism to make all the molecules needed by the organism is an active area of research.

Outcomes

1. Describe the structural building blocks of double stranded DNA.

2. Describe how the building blocks of RNA differs from DNA

3. Apply the central dogma of molecular biology to predict protein sequence from DNA sequence.

Plan

1. Form Nucleic Acid Teams. Assign team roles. Include a captain, spokesperson, reflector and recorder.

2. Answer Critical Thinking Questions.

3. As a group, use the information presented in the activity to make a generalization about intermolecular forces and DNA structure.

Information

DNA consists of two complimentary base-paired strands. The complimentary strands of DNA allow one strand to be used as a template for replication. Similarly, one strand of DNA is used as a template for the synthesis of RNA in transcription. The double helical DNA is a stable molecule; several important intermolecular forces are involved in maintaining its stability. The sequence of RNA is translated into protein; thus the amino acid sequence of a protein is prescribed by the sequence of bases in the DNA (see Model 1 on the following page).

Activity contributed by Kathleen Cornely.

Critical Thinking Questions

1. Which bases pair with one another in DNA? Classify each base as either a purine or pyrimidine. How many hydrogen bonds are formed between each of these pairs?

2. What is the name of the sugar found in DNA?

3. What is the name of the monomer that makes up the DNA polymer?

4. Are the complementary strands parallel or anti-parallel? How do you know?

5. List the intermolecular forces that are important in stabilizing the double helical structure. Indicate with a * which force(s) are more important. Do not dwell on this.

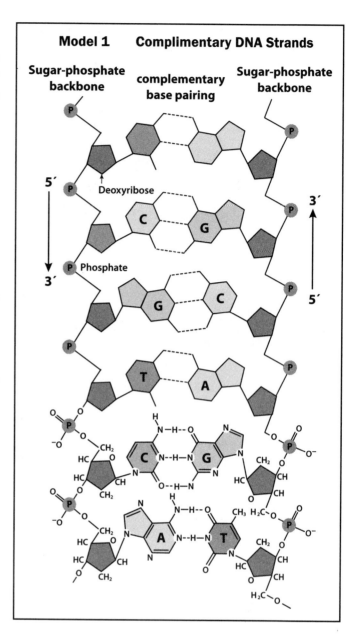

Model 1   Complimentary DNA Strands

6. Prior to the elucidation of the structure of DNA by Watson and Crick in 1953, Chargaff noted that the total amount of A + G in DNA is equal to the total amount of C + T, regardless of the source of the DNA. Explain the structural basis of this observation, knowing what we know now about the structure of DNA.

7. Explain why DNA denatures (separates into two strands) at pH > 11.

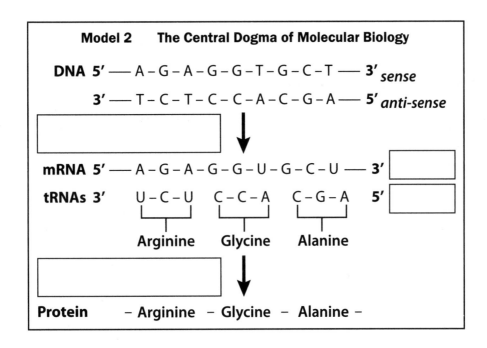

Model 2   The Central Dogma of Molecular Biology

DNA 5' — A – G – A – G – G – T – G – C – T — **3'** *sense*

3' — T – C – T – C – C – A – C – G – A — **5'** *anti-sense*

mRNA 5' — A – G – A – G – G – U – G – C – U — **3'**

tRNAs 3'   U – C – U   C – C – A   C – G – A   **5'**

Arginine   Glycine   Alanine

Protein   – Arginine – Glycine – Alanine –

8. Place the terms *transcripion*, *translation*, *codons* and *anticodons* in the appropriate boxes of Model 2, above.

9. From which strand is the mRNA synthesized, the sense strand or the antisense strand of the DNA?

10. How does the sense strand of the DNA differ from the structure of the mRNA? How is it alike?

11. How many consecutive nucleotides code for a single amino acid?

12. In which biopolymer (DNA, mRNA, tRNA or protein) would a mutation need to be located in order to be heritable and why?

1. Consult your textbook for the genetic code. Examine the following nucleotide sequence from the **sense** strand of DNA. What is the amino acid sequence of the encoded protein?

    ATG-CCT-TAC-GCC-CCT-GGA-GAC-GAA-AAG-AAG-GGT

2. A type of gene therapy called RNA interference (RNAi) is being investigated to treat Huntington's disease. This disease is the result of a mutation in the DNA that results in the synthesis of a nervous system protein with an altered amino acid sequence. The mutated protein forms clumps, which causes nervous system defects. To treat this disease, scientists synthesize short sequences of RNA (siRNA, or small interfering RNA) that forms base pairs with the mRNA that codes for the mutated protein.

    a. Design an siRNA that will interfere with the synthesis of the protein shown in Model 2.

    b. Explain how the addition of the siRNA will prevent the synthesis of the mutated protein.

    c. What are the difficulties that must be overcome in order for RNA interference to be an effective technique for treating the disease?

Section 18

Higher Order Structure of Nucleic Acids

PRE-ACTIVITY ASSIGNMENT

1. Produce a reading outline for the section in your textbook that discusses DNA and RNA structure.

2. Consider the single-stranded oligomer shown at right:

   a. Is this a piece of DNA or RNA? Justify your choice with two reasons.

   b. Circle a phosphate diester bond.

   c. Number the carbon atoms in the sugar moiety attached to the adenine.

   d. Draw the complementary strand showing the interactions between the base pairs.

IN-CLASS ACTIVITY

Why

DNA and RNA are responsible for the expression of genetic information in living systems. Slight differences in their monomeric structure lead to very different roles upon formation of higher order structure. A fundamental understanding of the intermolecular forces responsible for the structure of nucleic acids helps determine the functions of these macromolecules.

Outcomes

1. Describe the forces that drive the secondary structure of nucleic acids.

2. Compare and contrast DNA versus RNA structure.

3. Critically assess data in order to make general conclusions.

Plan

1. Team Manager should assign the roles of spokesperson, recorder, and reflector.

2. Answer the Critical Thinking Questions.

3. Prepare your spokesperson for class discussion, including any questions your group has for the instructor.

4. Identify the three most important insights your group discovered during this exercise. Have the spokesperson ready to share one of these with the whole class.

Activity contributed by Adam Cassano, Pamela Higgins, Bruce Heyen, and Susan White.

Critical Thinking Questions

1. Compare your answers to your reading questions in the assignment and come to a consensus.

2. a. Which is more hydrophobic—the sugar-phosphate backbone or the nitrogenous base pair?

   b. Predict which of these two components would be excluded in an aqueous environment.

3. Identify non-covalent interactions that occur between

   a. complementary base-pairs.

   b. consecutive base-pairs.

4. Explain how the orientation of the bases in the three-dimensional structure model contributes to the strength of the noncovalent interactions between consecutive base pairs.

5. The melting temperature of a population of DNA molecules is defined as the temperature at which fifty percent of the DNA becomes single-stranded. Consider the melting temperature data for the following DNA oligomers:

Double Stranded Oligomer	Number of Hydrogen Bonds	Relative Strength of Stacking interactions (1 = Strongest)	Melting Temperature
A A A A A A A A A T T T T T T T T T			11.3 °C
G A A A A A A A G C T T T T T T T C			15.6 °C
A A A A A A A A A A T T T T T T T T T T			15.9 °C

   a. Complete (Fill in) the table above.

   b. Interpret the melting temperature results based on the intermolecular interactions that drive the formation of double-stranded DNA.

c. Please examine the structures and data below. Note the samples are not identical in length and the bases in bold indicate a pairing of non-complementary basepairs. Do your conclusions that you made previously agree with the data below? Do you need to readjust your conclusions? Do so.

dsDNA sequence:	Tm
5´ -CTCTC**T**CTCTCTCTCTCTCTCT-3´ 3´ -GAGAG**T**GAGAGAGAGAGAGAGA-5´	18.0°C
5´ -CTCTCTCTCTCTCTCTCTCT-3´ 3´ -GAGAGAGAGAGAGAGAGAGA-5´	25.1°C

6. Single-stranded RNA also forms a helical structure. Describe the non-covalent forces that drive the formation of the single-stranded helix structure.

1. Ethidium bromide is a fluorescent molecule that interacts with DNA and is widely used in electrophoresis. Based on the structure of ethidium bromide, how does it interact with the DNA molecule and what effect would this interaction have with the melting temperature of the DNA? Justify your answer.

2. A ribosomal protein, L5, binds to a 5S-ribosomal RNA molecule. The specific secondary structure of ribosomal RNA that interacts with three tyrosine residues in the protein is shown. Would you expect the tyrosine residues to interact with the helix or the loop portion of this hairpin structure? Explain your answer.

Understanding the Rate Determining Step in a Metabolic Pathway

Why

In order to understand the generalized features of metabolic pathways one must understand how pathways work and how they integrate together. This activity places the concept of rate determining step within the context of metabolic pathways. Rate determining steps are key features in metabolic pathways and are key in understanding them.

Outcomes

1. Predict the effect of a pathway rate determining step (rds) on the accumulation of pathway intermediates.

2. Understand the flow of metabolic intermediates through a pathway and use the idea in future problems.

3. Communicate information about metabolic pathways using pathway diagrams.

Plan

1. Assign roles of team manager, reflector, and recorder. The manager is the person with the birthday farthest from today's date. The manager makes sure everyone is participating and watches the time, the reflector monitors how the group is functioning and if someone is dominating or not contributing. The reflector should be asked by the manager or other team members to provide feedback on team performance. The recorder should document group decisions and discoveries as well as participate.

2. Answer the Critical Thinking Questions.

3. As a group, reconsider the pathway diagrams you drew. Identify one or two ways in which they could be drawn differently to more clearly communicate relevant metabolic information.

Critical Thinking Questions

1. Discuss the term rate determining step as it was defined in general or organic chemistry.

2. Draw a pathway, called pathway A, with five molecules numbered 1 through 5. If the step from 2 to 3 is the rate determining step, what intermediate(s) will accumulate?

3. If the step from 4 to 5 is the rate determining step, what intermediate(s) will accumulate?

continued on next page

4. In pathway A (from question 2), what determines how fast substance 5 is made?

5. If the reaction rate of the rate determining step is decreased how will the speed with which substance 5 is made change?

6. The speed with which substance 5 is made is termed the metabolic flux of pathway A. Consider another pathway, called pathway B, which operates from molecules 5 to 1. It is a different pathway because a few of the enzymes used in pathway B catalyze different reactions than pathway A, even though the intermediates 1 through 5 are the identical to pathway A. The metabolic flux of pathway A is now complicated by the fact the molecule 5 could be used as starting materials in pathway B. Describe the possible changes in the flux of pathway A in the presence of pathway B. State all assumptions.

Foundations of Biochemistry

Understanding Metabolically Far From Equilibrium Reactions

PRE-ACTIVITY ASSIGNMENT

Produce a reading outline for the chapter giving an introductory overview of metabolism.

Before reading, review the learning objectives stated below so that you focus on essential material in your reading. You may find some answers in other parts of the book or not at all. Use other resources as necessary. Your discussion of the learning objectives below is your directed reading log for this material.

Learning Objectives: Introduction and Overview of Metabolism and Energetics

1. Distinguish between catabolism and anabolism.

2. Identify energy carriers (molecules) used directly for biosynthesis of simple molecules vs. macromolecules.

3. Within the context of metabolism, define what is meant by pathway.

4. Identify features common to metabolic pathways and locate these features within a given pathway.

5. Distinguish between a far from equilibrium reaction and a near equilibrium reaction.

6. Explain the chemical consequences of coupling a favorable reaction with an unfavorable one.

7. Define the term *metabolic flux.*

8. List the mechanisms by which pathways are regulated/controlled.

9. Distinguish between kinetic control and thermodynamic control of a reaction.

10. Distinguish between ΔG and ΔG° and $\Delta G'$.

11. Calculate any ΔG as above for an overall reaction.

12. Review and interpret velocity vs. [S] curves that are hyperbolic vs. sigmoidal.

continued on next page

Problem

Consider the following mini-pathway shown below:*

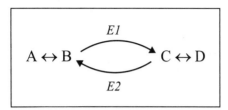

The pathway starts with substrate A and ends with substrate D. Substrate B is converted into C in a far from equilibrium reaction that involves more than just B and C although those are the only substances shown in the diagram. Conversion of C back into B requires a completely different pathway with different substances involved although they are not shown. The reaction B to C is catalyzed by enzyme E1 and the reaction from C to B is catalyzed by enzyme E2.

a. Under intracellular conditions the activity of E1 is 50 pmol of C created/10^6cells · s and that of E2 is 40 pmol of B created/10^6cells · s. What are the direction and overall rate of metabolic flux between B and C?

b. Calculate the overall rate of metabolic flux between B and C and the direction of the flux when each case below is true (consider the three cases to be independent of each other).

1. An inhibitor is used that reduces the activity of E1 by 10%,

2. An activator is used that increases the activity of E2 by 10%

3. The activity of E2 is doubled.

*adapted from *Biochemistry 3rd ed.*, Mathews and van Holde, 2000.

Why

An understanding of the generalized features of metabolic pathways is necessary in order to understand how pathways work and how they integrate together. Therefore, a solid mental picture of the features is needed. This activity focuses on those features that are new and difficult to appreciate.

Outcomes

1. Distinguish between near equilibrium and far from equilibrium reactions.

2. Explain why far from equilibrium reactions are the ones that are regulated.

Plan

1. Assign roles of manager, reflector, recorder. The manager is the person with the birthday closest to today's date. The manager makes sure every one is participating and watches the time. The reflector monitors how the group is functioning, if someone is dominating or not contributing. The reflector should be asked by the manager or other team members to provide feedback on team performance. The recorder documents group decisions and discoveries as well as participates.

2. Answer the Critical Thinking Questions.

3. Generate two questions the group has about this activity to share with the class.

4. Make two generalizations about metabolically irreversible reactions to share.

Critical Thinking Questions

1. Identify the criteria for a system to be at equilibrium.

2. Does the actual concentration of metabolites affect $\Delta G'$? $\Delta G^{\circ'}$?

3. Metabolically far from equilibrium reactions are said to be "metabolically irreversible." What do you think that means? Be sure to consider free energy (magnitude and sign) and reactant/product concentrations in your answer.

continued on next page

4. Using the figure below, circle the reactions that are near equilibrium. Justify your choices.

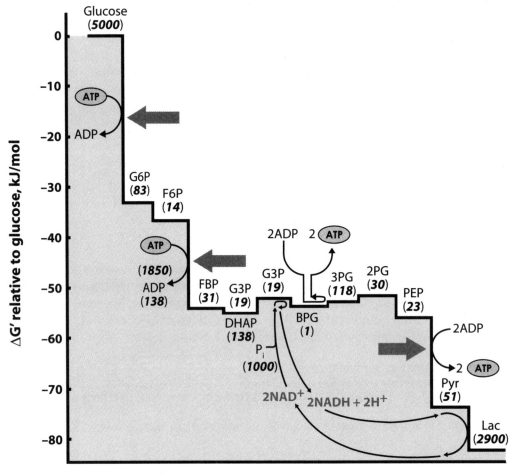

Pathway progress

Note: The numbers in parenthesis are the approximate micromolar concentrations in the cell.

5. Using the same figure, box the reactions that are far from equilibrium. Justify your choices.

Foundations of Biochemistry

6. Your homework assignment on bioenergetics illustrated a metabolically far from equilibrium reaction from B to C. Notice that going from B to C uses a **different** reaction (and therefore a different enzyme) than going from C to B. This is typical of metabolically far from equilibrium reactions. The reactions with the large arrows in the question 4 figure behave like B to C in the homework problem. Two actual reactions that follow this pattern in glycolysis (the breakdown of glucose) and gluconeogenesis (the synthesis of glucose) are shown below. How do these reactions look like the reverse of each other and how are they not the reverse?

Hexokinase

Glycolysis   Glucose + ATP $\longrightarrow$ glucose-6-phosphate + ADP $\Delta G^{\circ\prime} = -16\text{kJ/mol}$

G-6-P phosphatase

Gluconeogenesis   Glucose-6-phosphate + H_2O $\longrightarrow$ glucose + PO_4^{3-} $\Delta G^{\circ\prime} = -12\text{kJ/mol}$

7. Why are the above reactions metabolically irreversible? Would these far from equilibrium reactions be irreversible outside the context of a metabolic pathway? How could you test your assertion?

1. Reactions in metabolic pathways that are far from equilibrium are regulation points in the pathway. This phenomenon is not a biological coincidence. In fact, cells actively maintain these select reactions at conditions that are far from equilibrium. Without such regulation, metabolism could easily become an uncontrollable tangle of ultimately unproductive reactions. One way that cells maintain far from equilibrium concentrations of metabolic intermediates is by compartmentalization using membranes.

   a. Name at least four metabolically significant membrane bound cellular compartments and the metabolic pathway(s) that take place within each compartment.

   b. Based on your knowledge of membrane characteristics, would you expect the metabolic substrates and cofactors glucose, pyruvate, ATP, NADH, and FAD to transit across membranes? Explain your reasoning, including specific reference to chemical characteristics of these molecules. Be sure to consider whether transit would be controlled or uncontrolled.

Foundations of Biochemistry

High Energy Compounds

Why

There is much confusion about the topic of energy and ATP in biochemical systems. It is important to learn the proper terminology for describing the energy used in cells.

Outcomes

1. Be able to discuss cellular energy using correct terminology.

2. Be able to describe where the energy comes from.

3. Develop the ability to think critically about your assumptions.

Plan

1. Complete the following activity. Use the spy role as needed to ask for help from others.

2. As a group, identify any assumptions you made in solving this problem.

3. Identify the most important thing you learned about problem solving today that will help you solve new problems.

Check Your Prior Knowledge

Answer the following TRUE or FALSE. Check your answers with the instructor before moving on.

1. ____F____ Breaking any bond is always exothermic.

2. ____T____ Breaking any bond is always endothermic.

3. ____F____ Whether breaking a bond is endothermic or exothermic depends on the bond.

4. ____F____ Any reaction that involves ATP as a reactant will have a large negative ΔG.
   ↳ depends on what the other reaction is

ALWAYS TAKES ENERGY TO BREAK A BOND

continued on next page

Critical Thinking Question

Given below are the balanced chemical equation for the hydrolysis of ATP and the structure of ATP. Refer to these to answer the following question.

$$ATP^{4-} + H_2O \rightarrow ADP^{3-} + HPO_4^{2-} + H^+$$

1. Your task is to explain the source of Gibbs free energy in terms of the changes in molecular structure when ATP reacts with water. Consider bond energies, resonance stabilization, and charge destabilization.

- charge separation
- Entropy increases
- P more soluble in H_2O
- Products are resonance stabilized

Section 22

Enzymes in Glycolysis

PRE-ACTIVITY **ASSIGNMENT**

1. Produce a reading outline for the chapter in your textbook on glycolysis.

2. Review allosteric control of enzyme activity.

3. For the figure below, use the box provided to label the reactions that are:

P — Phosphorylations   **I** — Isomerizations

O — Oxidation reactions   **D** — Dehydrations

C — C-C bond cleavage   **F** — Far from equilibrium

E — Equilibrium   **A** — make ATP

For most of these you should be able to make the determination based on your prior knowledge from organic chemistry. For the far from equilibrium reactions and the ATP generating reaction you will need to use your book or the figure below.

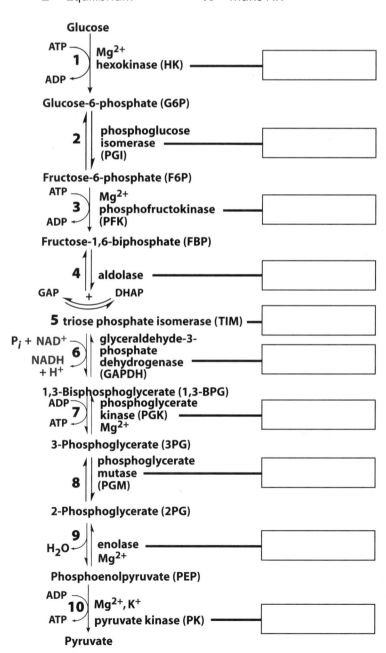

4. Which reactions are different in gluconeo-genesis? How do you know? (Use the numbers of the reactions.)

91

Why

The regulation of enzymes is what controls the general flow of metabolites through the pathways of metabolism. Metabolic flux of pathways is controlled by numerous mechanisms involving the rate-controlling enzymes in the pathway. The two regulatory mechanisms we examine here are small molecules that act as allosteric effectors and isoenzymes (isoforms).

Outcomes

1. Interpret the impact of different K_m values in real situations.

2. Describe how isoenzymes and allosteric effectors play important roles in regulation of pathways.

3. Communicate using graphics. Specifically, create a graph from information provided as text.

Plan

1. Form teams, assume a new role in your team.

2. Answer the Critical Thinking Questions.

3. Did everyone in your group contribute to the activity today? If so, explain how. If not, make a plan to improve participation.

Information

Characteristics of hexokinase isoform in most cells

- low K_m for sugars (0.1mM)
- broad specificity for sugars
- inhibited by glucose-6-phosphate
- the [glucose] $_{intracellular}$ >>> K_m; the intracellular [glucose] ~ 5mM

Characterictics of the hexokinase isoform in liver cells (called glucokinase)

- very high K_m for sugars (10mM)
- broad specificity for sugars
- sigmoidal concentration dependence on glucose
- no inhibition by glucose-6-phosphate

Critical Thinking Questions

1. Review allosteric control of enzyme activity. You may need to refer to sections of your book not assigned in your preparatory reading.

2. Translate the information provided in this activity into two line graphs of *v* vs. [glucose] for both hexokinase and its isoenzyme glucokinase on the same plot. For simplicity, assume the same V_{max} for both enzymes. Include curves for each enzyme in the presence and absence of G-6-P. What type of inhibition might you expect from G-6-P? Competitive? Allosteric? Select one, explain your reasoning, and use that to draw your curve.

3. The function of the liver in humans is to maintain the [glucose] circulating in the blood stream at reasonably constant levels. This is so organs like the brain that use primarily glucose as their carbon source to produce energy via ATP have a steady supply of glucose. It also ensures that the levels of glucose in the blood stream do not get too high. Using the plots from question 2, discuss why it makes sense that glucokinase in liver would behave differently than the hexokinase in other cells.

4. Discuss why the inhibition of hexokinase by G-6-P makes sense.

5. Hexokinase is also inhibited by ATP (its substrate). Why does this make sense?

6. What features of an isoenzyme permit one isoform to be inhibited and another not to be inhibited?

1. Reread the section in your textbook on allosteric regulation of enzymes. Discuss the advantages of isoenzymes for different tissues. Be sure to mention something about allosteric modifiers in your answer.

2. Using the graph below, indicate on the curve the range of intracellular substrate concentrations that would result in optimal effectiveness in the regulation of enzyme activity by substrate availability. Discuss your choice.

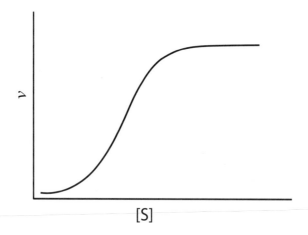

3. Phosphofructokinase-1 is the main flux controlling enzyme for glycolysis. It is inhibited by high [ATP]. There exist metabolic circumstances in which the inhibition by ATP is overridden. Draw v vs. [S] graphs showing the inhibition of PFK-1 activity by ATP and the circumstance in which the inhibition by ATP is overridden.

Section 23

Regulation of Glycolysis and Gluconeogenesis

PRE-ACTIVITY ASSIGNMENT

1. Produce a reading outline for the section in your textbook on gluconeogenesis.

2. The carbons in glucose are numbered from the anomeric carbon. What are the glucose numbers for the carbons in GAP? in DHAP? If TIM isomerizes GAP to DHAP what are the glucose numbers for the carbons in DHAP now?

3. Label the carbons in pyruvate relative to the carbons from which they were derived in glucose (for example carbon 1 from glucose is found at which location in pyruvate). Do not use the labeling system derived from organic chemistry where the carbonyl would be carbon 1 in all compounds with a carbonyl—use the carbon numbers from glucose.

4. What is the role of the liver in glucose metabolism? What is the role of the muscle in glucose metabolism? Refer to chapters on physiology and metabolism as needed.

5. In what cellular compartment do most of the reactions of glycolysis take place?

IN-CLASS ACTIVITY

Why

It is important to understand the role of the liver in glycolysis, in gluconeogenesis, and in the body. To do this we will examine the gluconeogenesis pathway in light of your understanding of glycolysis and the role of the liver and the muscle in the body.

Outcomes

1. Understand the roles of muscle and liver in glycolysis and gluconeogensis.

2. Understand isoenzymes and their role in regulation of glucose synthesis and catabolism.

3. Develop the ability to think critically about the link between the macroscopic (organ function) and the microscopic (metabolism of glucose).

4. Manage team members with different levels of biology knowledge.

Plan

1. Begin by making sure everyone agrees on the assignment completed for today.

2. Answer the Critical Thinking Questions.

3. Summarize the objectives of today's activity. Identify the content you were supposed to learn and how well you mastered it.

continued on next page

95

Critical Thinking Questions

1. What reaction does pyruvate kinase catalyze? Draw out the reaction.

2. At what step in glycolysis does this reaction happen?

3. What are the roles of the liver and the muscle in our bodies?

4. What is the role of glucose metabolism in the liver and muscle?

5. It has been shown that muscle pyruvate kinase (PK) responds hyperbolically to its substrate, PEP, but the liver form of the enzyme responds sigmoidally. Fructose-1,6-bisphosphate is an allosteric activator of liver PK, but it apparently has no effect on the muscle enzyme.

   a. Sketch velocity versus substrate concentration graphs for both liver and muscle PK including the F-1,6-BP effect. Discuss why this regulation makes sense.

b. What is the metabolic advantage of having the liver PK activated by fructose-1,6-bisphosphate?

c. If the liver PK responded hyperbolically to PEP and were otherwise unregulated, how might gluconeogenesis be affected?

6. What reactions are used to circumvent the pyruvate kinase reaction in liver gluconeogenesis?

7. What reaction does phosphofructokinase-1 catalyze?

8. What reaction is used to circumvent PFK-1 in gluconeogenesis?

9. How does the small molecule fructose-2,6-bisphosphate alter the activities of PFK-1 and fructose-1,6-bisphosphatase?

1. In the conversion of pyruvate (PYR) to phosphoenolpyruvate (PEP) in gluconeogenesis, the addition of CO_2 is followed by a decarboxylation. Why would nature add the CO_2 only to remove it in the next step? Is the carbon added the same as the one removed?

2. ^{14}C-glucose (with ONLY carbon 5 radioactively labeled 5-^{14}C-glucose) is given to metabolically active liver cells in cell culture. The cells are isolated after a short time and the glucose-6-phosphate of the cells analyzed. The glucose-6-phosphate contains the ^{14}C label in the carbon 5 and carbon 2 positions. Explain these observations.

Metabolic and Hormonal Control in Glycolysis and Gluconeogenesis

1. Review sections on glycolysis and gluconeogenesis in your textbook paying particular attention to hormonal control of these pathways. If your textbook has a section on hormonal control, produce a reading outline on this section.

2. What are the body conditions that result in the release of the hormones glucagon and epinephrine?

3. List which reactions in glycolysis and gluconeogenesis are affected in the liver indirectly by the hormones glucagon and epinephrine.

IN-CLASS ACTIVITY

Why

PFK-1 in glycolysis and F-1,6-BPase in gluconeogenesis are major control points in liver cells. These reactions contribute to the flux through these pathways and studying their regulation serves as a model for understanding metabolic and hormonal control of metabolism in general.

Outcomes

1. Describe reciprocal regulation in words and with plots.

2. Compare and contrast metabolic and hormonal regulation.

3. Compare the roles and regulation of these pathways in muscle and liver.

Plan

1. Form teams and assign roles.

2. Complete Critical Thinking Questions.

3. As a group, identify two questions that remain after today's activity and plan a strategy to answer them.

Critical Thinking Questions

1. Draw the *v* vs [S] plots for phosphofructokinase-1 with and without fructose-2,6-bisphosphate. The first is hyberbolic and the second is sigmoidal.

2. Draw the *v* vs [S] plots for phosphofructokinase-1 with high and low [ATP]. The second is hyberbolic and the first is sigmoidal.

3. Answer the following questions about reverse reactions and reverse pathways:

   a. Define the terms reverse reaction and reverse pathway. Compare and contrast these two terms.

   b. Consider the reaction from fructose-6-phosphate to fructose-1,6-bisphosphate in glycolysis and back again in gluconeogenesis. They are said to be reciprocally regulated. What does that mean? Use one or both of the terms defined in question 3a correctly in your answer.

c. The two reactions in part b are called a *substrate cycle* or *futile cycle*. What does that mean?

4. Predict the *v* vs. [S] plot for fructose-1,6-bisphosphatase in the presence and absence of fructose-2,6-bisphosphate.

5. Would epinephrine have the same effect as glucagon in the liver? Does the liver have epinephrine receptors? Glucagon receptors?

6. What effect would glucagon have in muscle? Does the muscle have glucagon receptors?

7. What effect would epinephrine have in muscle?

8. Briefly describe what happens inside a cell as a result of a hormone signal.

9. What distinguishes metabolic control from hormonal control? Consider that AMP, ATP and citrate are metabolic effectors whereas fructose-2,6-bisphosphate is produced primarily from a hormone signal.

1. Gluconeogenesis in the liver can utilize different precursors depending on what is happening elsewhere in the body. The liver can use lactate, which comes from the muscle during exertion and after exercise. It can also indirectly use alanine.

    a. What needs to happen in order for alanine to be used for gluconeogenesis?

    b. Under what conditions might alanine be the precursor for gluconeogenesis?

2. The precursors to gluconeogenesis including acetyl Co-A and pyruvate can act as allosteric effectors to modulate the activity of PK, PEPCK, and pyruvate carboxylase. Describe the metabolic effects and the impact on a whole animal if the following mutations were present in the liver isoforms of the enzymes listed below.

    a. The allosteric binding site for alanine on pyruvate kinase is mutated, decreasing affinity for alanine.

    b. The regulatory phosphorylation site on pyruvate kinase is eliminated through a single amino acid mutation.

    c. The allosteric binding site for acetyl-CoA on pyruvate carboxylase is mutated, decreasing affinity for acetyl-CoA.

    d. The pyruvate carboxylase gene is mutated resulting in an enzyme that is catalytically inactive. (HINT: Is there another cellular source of OAA?)

    e. The PEPCK gene is mutated resulting in an enzyme that is catalytically inactive.

Regulation of Glycogen Storage and Breakdown

PRE-ACTIVITY ASSIGNMENT

1. Produce a reading outline for the section on glycogen in your textbook.

2. Review the figure below, which diagrams the glycogen metabolism enzymes in muscle. The hormone epinephrine is not shown in the figure. Where should it be? Which enzymes become phosphorylated as a result of the hormone signal? Which enzymes become active as a result of the hormone signal? Would you expect regulation by phosphorylation or allosteric control to be more responsive to subtle changes in cellular conditions?

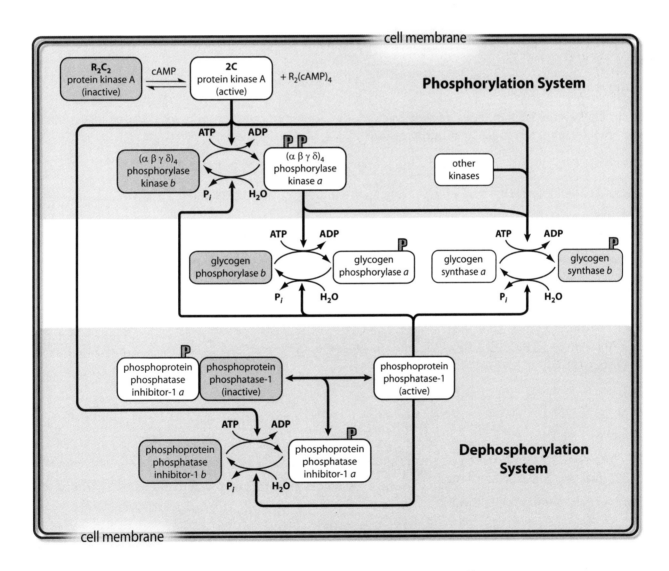

Why

Cellular glycogen metabolism is regulated by allosteric control and covalent modification of enzymes involved in reciprocal pathways. Therefore glycogen metabolism can be considered a model of these types of regulation.

Outcomes

1. Distinguish between allosteric control and covalent modification as regulatory mechanisms.

2. Describe how covalent modification of enzymes can lead to amplification of a biochemical signal.

3. Explain the flexibility inherent in regulatory cascades.

4. Develop the abilities to identify and use diverse backgrounds of group members to solve interdisciplinary problems.

Plan

1. Form teams and assign roles.

2. This activity requires some specific biology knowledge. Identify group members with prior biology coursework and make a plan to ensure their participation.

3. Complete Critical Thinking Questions and prepare spokesperson to report out.

4. Record questions you have so we can address them today or next class period.

Critical Thinking Questions

1. Review your assignment for today and answer questions you have within your group.

2. Define allosteric control. Give an example of allosteric control from glycogen synthesis or breakdown pathways

3. Define *control by covalent modification*. Give an example of control by covalent modification from glycogen synthesis or breakdown pathways.

4. Compare and contrast covalent modification versus allosteric control as effectors of enzyme activity. Be sure to address the following in your response.

  a. Write reactions that show a general enzyme before and after covalent modification and before and after allosteric interactions.

  b. For each case above, what is directly responsible for creating the "after" situation? Is it a product of the cellular conditions, enzyme activity, or something else?

  c. How can the effects shown in the reactions in question 4a be reversed?

5. Mutations in genes sometimes result in problems with metabolic regulation.
  a. Do mutations always result in loss of protein function? If not, describe the other possibilities.

  b. Using phosphorylation as an example, describe the possible effects of a single amino acid mutation (one amino acid is different between normal and mutant proteins) on covalent regulation of metabolism. As part of your answer, state your assumptions about identity of the amino acids under normal conditions and in a cell expressing the mutant protein.

  c. Describe the effects of a single amino acid mutation on allosteric regulation of metabolism.

continued on next page

6. Use glycogen phosphorylase to illustrate how covalent modification can override allosteric control.

1. Predict the *v* vs. [S] plot for fructose-1,6-bisphosphatase in presence of high and low [AMP].

2. Explain why phosphorylation/dephosphorylation of metabolic enzymes through cyclic cascades is viewed as a more sensitive regulation system than allosteric control. Use specific examples to help make your point. Define the term *sensitive* as part of your response.

Glycolysis and Gluconeogenesis Problem Solving

1. List all the possible reactions of pyruvate.

2. What is the role of the pyruvate to lactate reaction in keeping glycolysis operating? Why would glycolysis need to keep running?

Why

Metabolism is most interesting in context; these problems provide an opportunity to apply what you have learned to the real world.

Outcomes

1. Apply basic understanding of glycolysis and gluconeogenesis to real world problems.

2. Gain skills and confidence in solving complex, open-ended problems.

3. Develop your ability to communicate solutions clearly and concisely.

Plan

1. Complete the first problem using your standard group approach to answering questions.

2. Complete and record an exam-quality response to the second question.

3. Have the spokesperson read the written responses to the group. Identify one strength and one area for improvement.

4. Turn in one response per team for comments.

Critical Thinking Questions (*Problems*)

1. Anybody who has exercised strenuously has experienced lactic acid build up in the muscles. Excess lactic acid is generated when the rate or flux of glycolysis exceeds the capacity of the citric acid cycle to more completely oxidize the pyruvate to CO_2. Actually it has been shown that even in excess O_2 a large fraction of pyruvate goes to lactate in muscle—there just are not enough mitochondria in muscle.

   Knowing that exerting muscles rely on glycolysis for ATP, what would be the effect of a drug that inhibits lactate dehydrogenase? Would you expect the effect of a drug that inhibits lactate transport proteins to be the same or different? Explain.

2. The enzyme, which catalyzes the pyruvate to lactate reversible conversion, is called lactate dehydrogenase, LDH. It is a tetrameric enzyme composed of two subunit types, M and H. The enzyme form in the heart is H4 and the muscle form is M4. The heart cells are loaded with mitochondria and are capable of very high rates of the citric acid cycle much more so than muscle cells (afterall, the heart does not take a break, but muscle cells do). The heart isoenzyme of LDH is strongly inhibited allosterically by pyruvate whereas the muscle enzyme is not inhibited at all. Provide a metabolic explanation for these observations taking into account the function of these two tissues types.

Glycolysis and Gluconeogenesis Problem Solving 2

IN-CLASS **ACTIVITY**

Why

Metabolism is most interesting in context these problems provide an opportunity to apply what you have learned to the real world.

Outcomes

1. Apply basic understanding of glycolysis and gluconeogenesis to real world problems.

2. Gain skills and confidence in solving complex, open-ended problems.

3. Develop your ability to communicate solutions clearly and concisely.

Plan

1. Record brief answers for 1a through e. Record an exam-quality answer for 1f.

2. Record an exam-quality answer for 2.

3. Have the spokesperson read the exam-quality responses to the group. Identify one strength and one area for improvement.

4. Turn in one response per team for comments.

Critical Thinking Questions (*Problems*)

1. When we ingest fructose, as we often do with high fructose corn syrup drinks, the fructose is metabolized differently than other sugars by the liver. The fructose is transported into the liver where it is directly phosphorylated to form fructose-1-phosphate. This fructose phosphate then undergoes an aldol cleavage to yield dihydroxyacetone phosphate (DHAP) and glyceraldehyde. The glyceraldehyde is then phosphorylated to form GAP. This alternative pathway is only found in the liver. As you discussed in your groups, muscle pyruvate kinase responds hyperbolically to its substrate PEP, whereas the liver enzyme responds sigmoidally. In addition the liver pyruvate kinase is activated by F-1,6-BP.

    a. Draw the curve for liver pyruvate kinase. Put appropriate labels (the actual labels rather than just *v* and *S*) on your graph.

continued on next page

b. What is the main metabolic role of the liver?

c. What would cause high levels of PEP in the liver?

d. Does the metabolism of fructose outlined in question 1 proceed through the committed step of glycolysis? Explain <u>briefly</u>.

e. Will F-1,6-BP be generated in the liver? Specifically explain why or why not.

f. Explain the kinetics of liver pyruvate kinase activity in light of the alternative pathway (question 1) and in light of the liver's role in glycolysis and gluconeogenesis.

2. Red blood cells synthesize and degrade 2,3-BPG as a detour from the glycolytic pathway, as shown in the figure below:

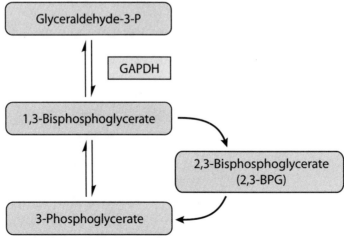

2,3-BPG decreases the oxygen affinity of hemoglobin by binding in the central cavity of the deoxygenated form of hemoglobin. This encourages delivery of oxygen to tissues. A defect in one of the glycolytic enzymes may affect the levels of 2,3-BPG. The graph below shows the oxygen-binding curve for normal erythrocytes.

a. Based on your understanding of the role of 2,3-BPG in the affinity of hemoglobin for oxygen and using the graph below, predict and draw the oxygen binding curve for pyruvate kinase deficient erythrocytes and explain your choice.

b. Based on your understanding of the role of 2,3-BPG in the affinity of hemoglobin for oxygen and using the graph below, predict and draw the oxygen binding curve for hexokinase deficient erythrocytes and explain your choice.

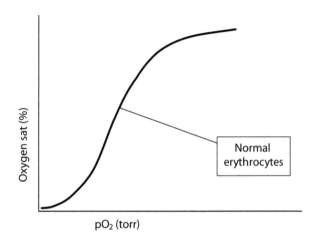

(This page intentionally left blank.)

Section 28

Pentose Phosphate Pathway

PRE-ACTIVITY ASSIGNMENT

1. Produce a reading outline for the section in your textbook on the pentose phosphate pathway.

2. Explain how you know the carbon in CO_2 is more oxidized than in glucose.

3. Draw the structures of glucose and pyruvate. Label the carbons in glucose 1-6 . Label the corresponding carbons in pyruvate, keeping in mind that each carbon in pyruvate will have two numbers.

IN-CLASS ACTIVITY

Why

The pentose phosphate pathway represents an alternative pathway to oxidize glucose to CO_2 that is different from the combined effects of glycolysis and the citric acid cycle. While glycolysis produces ATP and carbon fragments for further oxidation to CO_2 in the citric acid cycle or for biosynthetic pathways, the pentose phosphate pathway directly provides reducing power (NADPH), CO_2 and carbon molecule precursors for biosynthetic pathways. The extent to which each pathway processes glucose provides a window into the needs of the cell that can be monitored experimentally by the measurement of ^{14}C-CO_2 from ^{14}C-glucose. In this activity we will examine the products provided to the cell by the pentose phosphate pathway.

Outcomes

1. Be able to predict the biochemical route followed by glucose molecules to optimize production of the various products of the pentose phosphate pathway.

2. Know which carbons from glucose form CO_2 in this pathway.

3. State those biochemical processes in which NADPH is important.

4. Develop your ability to transfer knowledge from one context to another.

Plan

1. Form teams.

2. Complete Critical Thinking Questions and prepare spokesperson to report out.

3. In your team, reflect on how the Pentose Phosphate Pathway is similar to and different from glycolysis.

Critical Thinking Questions

1. Be sure you have all read the Why section.

2. Where does the pentose phosphate pathway branch from glycolysis? At what molecule?

continued on next page

3. Is that molecule part of a metabolic pool? With what other molecule?

4. At what molecule does the pathway return into glycolysis?

5. What is the cellular role of NADPH? Under what conditions or in what cells is NADPH produced in substantial amounts?

6. In what pathways is ATP produced? NADPH produced? Ribose-5-phosphate produced?

7. What is the reaction that controls the entry of glucose carbons into the pentose phosphate pathway? How is this reaction regulated?

8. When the cellular demand for NADPH is greater than the cellular demand for ribose-5-P and ATP, how is G-6-P metabolized?

9. When the cellular demand for NADPH and ATP are high compared to ribose-5-P, how is G-6-P metabolized?

10. When the cellular demand for ribose-5-P is greater than NADPH and ATP, how is G-6-P metabolized? Consider your answer to question 7 and assume NADPH levels are high.

11. What is the cellular role of glutathione and how is it related to NADPH?

Use this Information for question 12:

Many metabolic experiments are performed using substrates containing radioactive isotopes such as ^{14}C. Substrates, for example glucose, can be synthesized with radioactive isotopes in known locations within a molecule. Specifically, six different glucose molecules could be made with a different carbon labeled in each position. It is known that glucose can be metabolized to a variety of products including pyruvate, carbon dioxide, and others through several different pathways such as glycolysis and the citric acid cycle. By knowing which carbon is labeled in a given experiment, scientists can learn something about metabolic pathways used under given conditions by detecting radiolabel in some metabolic end products but not others. In a typical experiment, cells would be exposed to a radiolabeled substrate for a finite period of time after which the desired metabolic product, for example carbon dioxide, would be collected and measured for radioactivity.

12. Which carbon would need to be labeled in glucose in order for it to be detected in carbon dioxide as an indicator of glucose entry into the pentose phosphate pathway?

Foundations of Biochemistry

Exploring Pyruvate Dehydrogenase and the Citric Acid Cycle

PRE-ACTIVITY ASSIGNMENT

Prepare a reading outline for the section in your textbook on pyruvate dehydrogenase. Study a detailed figure in your book on the citric acid cycle and produce a reading outline for the section in your textbook that gives an overview of the citric acid cycle.

The following activity and skill exercise rely partially on data from a paper published in the *Journal of Biological Chemistry*.

- **To prepare, read the following summary of the relevant points of the paper and review the data in Tables I and II.**
- **What are [1-^{14}C]-Glc, [3,4-^{14}C]-Glc, [6-^{14}C]-Glc, and [U-^{14}C]-Glc?**

Many metabolic experiments are performed using substrates containing radioactive isotopes such as ^{14}C. Substrates, for example glucose, can be synthesized with radioactive isotopes in known locations within a molecule. Specifically, six different glucose molecules could be made with a different carbon labeled in each position. It is known that glucose can be metabolized to a variety of products including pyruvate, carbon dioxide, and others through several different pathways such as glycolysis and the citric acid cycle. By knowing which carbon is labeled in a given experiment, scientists can learn something about metabolic pathways used under given conditions by detecting radiolabel in some metabolic end products but not others. In a typical experiment, cells would be exposed to a radiolabeled substrate for a finite period of time after which the desired metabolic product, for example carbon dioxide, would be collected and measured for radioactivity. The above-described approach is used in a paper entitled "Glucose is Essential for Proliferation and the Glycolytic Enzyme Induction that Provokes a Transition to Glycolytic Energy Production" (Greiner, E., Guppy, M., and Brand, K. (1994) *J. Biol. Chem.* 269, 31484-31490. This article is available free on the web at www.jbc.org if you wish to download a PDF of the entire document).

It is known that tumor cells have a high rate of glycolysis even under aerobic conditions. This is surprising since glycolysis typically dominates under anaerobic conditions, whereas the citric acid cycle and oxidative phosphorylation dominate under aerobic conditions. As early as the 1920's, Warburg and co-workers observed this phenomenon in tumor cells, which they called "aerobic glycolysis" Warburg hypothesized that part of the transition from normal to tumor cells resulted in damage to mitochondria, impairing oxidative phosphylation. A few years later, Crabtree and coworkers showed that addition of glucose to tumor cells results in the inhibition of oxygen consumption, a phenomenon called the "Crabtree effect." Elucidating the molecular basis of the Crabtree effect is important because understanding unique aspects of tumor cell metabolism could lead to effective, tumor-specific drug therapies.

In order to better understand which metabolic pathways are active in tumor cells, the authors of this paper use a model system, proliferating thymocytes. Although the thymocytes used in this study are not cancerous, they provide a good model for cancer cells, which have high proliferation rates. Furthermore, proliferating thymocytes have an obvious control, non-proliferating (resting) thymocytes, which behave like normal, non-cancerous cells. To answer the question, "what is the mechanism by which glycolytic enzymes are induced in proliferating rat thymocytes during the transition from aerobic to anaerobic glucose metabolism," this article looks at the combined effects of glycolysis and the subsequent fate of pyruvate into either lactate or the citric acid cycle and oxidative phosphorylation OR glucose being routed into the pentose phosphate pathway.

continued on next page

The method for introducing labeled glucose and detecting $^{14}C-CO_2$ is as follows: The cells and an O_2/CO_2 mixture (19:1) were shaken continuously and the uptake of radioactive glucose terminated by addition of 1M $HClO_4$. The $^{14}C-CO_2$ evolved was trapped in 0.5 mL of 2-phenethylamine and the radioactivity was counted. Their pilot studies showed that ^{14}C-glucose utilization and $^{14}C-CO_2$ release were linear up to 3 hours. A condensed version of data tables from the paper is given below:

Table I: Glucose concentration in all incubations was 4 mM. Mean values ±S.E. are given in $\mu mol/10^{10}$ cells/h from eight separate experiments.

Conditions	Glucose consumption	Lactate production	$^{14}CO_2$ production from [1-^{14}C]-Glc	$^{14}CO_2$ production from [3,4-^{14}C]-Glc	$^{14}CO_2$ production from [6-^{14}C]-Glc	$^{14}CO_2$ production from [U-^{14}C]-Glc
Resting Thymocytes	42.6 ± 1.23	37.2 ± 2.51	5.10 ± 0.51	21.3 ± 2.18	1.98 ± 0.19	38.6 ± 2.16
Proliferating Thymocytes	740 ± 5.09	1320 ± 88.6	11.6 ± 1.01	20.1 ± 2.15	0.93 ± 0.06	36.1 ± 3.24

Table II: The ratio (6-^{14}C-labeled glucose to $^{14}CO_2$/3,4-^{14}C-labeled glucose to $^{14}CO_2$) serves to estimate the activity of the citric acid cycle in relation to the glucose flux through pyruvate dehydrogenase. The calculation is based on the assumption that funneling of pyruvate into the citric acid cycle is exclusively catalyzed by the pyruvate dehydrogenase reaction.

	Resting Thymocytes	Proliferating Thymocytes
$\dfrac{^{14}CO_2 \text{ from } 6\text{-}^{14}C\text{-glucose}}{^{14}CO_2 \text{ from } 3,4\text{-}^{14}C\text{-glucose}}$	0.19	0.093

Why

There are multiple points of entry and exit for carbon molecules into the central metabolic pathway of the citric acid cycle (also know as the tricarboxylic acid cycle, TCA cycle, or Kreb's cycle). The citric acid cycle is central to the metabolism of fats and much of glucose and many amino acids. Therefore the functioning of the cycle is critical to your understanding of integrated metabolism since much passes through the cycle.

Outcomes

1. Know the reactions that pyruvate can undergo and use your understanding of cellular needs to predict which reaction will occur.

2. Know which carbons from glucose form CO_2 in this pathway and to use that knowledge to interpret ^{14}C-CO_2 data.

3. Build specific knowledge to understand the citric acid cycle.

4. Process metabolic data presented in a table and use it to make generalizations about cell-specific metabolic activity.

Plan

1. Assign roles.

2. Assign someone to be the skeptic today. Ask if you are uncertain of this role.

3. Reflect on your group's ability to process the tabular information presented in this activity. What did you do well? What changes could you make to help you better process information presented in tables in the future?

4. Complete Critical Thinking Questions and prepare spokesperson to report out.

Critical Thinking Questions

1. The reaction catalyzed by the pyruvate dehydrogenase complex (PYR DH) is a reaction that is under extensive regulation by allosteric control and covalent modification since the acetyl CoA it produces is a main entry point of carbons into the citric acid cycle. The complex is a multienzyme complex. What does that term mean? How many different enzymes are there? What might be the advantage(s) of a multienzyme complex?

2. The PYR DH complex requires five coenzymes. What distinguishes a coenzyme from an enzyme?

3. Coenzyme A (CoA) forms a thioester with the acetyl group derived from pyruvate after decarboxylation. Is the hydrolysis of a thioester more or less energetically favorable than the hydrolysis of a simple ester? Explain.

continued on next page

Section 29 — Exploring Pyruvate Dehydrogenase and the Citric Acid Cycle

4. Since carbons arrive from glucose via acetyl CoA, what carbons from glucose are in acetyl CoA? Number them in acetyl CoA using the original numbers from glucose.

5. Are any carbons from acetyl CoA removed as CO_2 during the first "turn" of the citric acid cycle? Explain.

6. What glucose carbon(s) is (are) the first to be removed as CO_2 in the citric acid cycle?

Refer to Information in your Assignment to answer questions 7–11:

7. Which carbons would need to be labeled in glucose in order to detect radioactivity in carbon dioxide produced in the reaction catalyzed by pyruvate dehydrogenase?

8. ^{14}C-CO_2 produced from 3-^{14}C-glucose will indicate that radiolabeled glucose proceeded through one major metabolic pathway. Which pathway? Explain how you know.

9. Would carbon from 3-^{14}C-glucose show up in CO_2 generated from the citric acid cycle?

10. Why does the ratio of $\dfrac{^{14}CO_2 \text{ from } 6\text{-}^{14}C\text{-glucose}}{^{14}CO_2 \text{ from } 3,4\text{-}^{14}C\text{-glucose}}$ provide an estimate of citric acid cycle flux relative to glycolysis flux (or metabolism)?

11. Why don't you obtain the reported 0.19 for the ratio in resting cells in Table II from the article when you divide 1.98 by 21.3 from Table I? Or the 0.093 for the proliferating cells?

12. Why is it reasonable to take the amount of ^{14}C-CO_2 produced from 1-^{14}C-glucose minus the amount of ^{14}C-CO_2 produced from 6-^{14}C-glucose as a measure of the pentose phosphate shunt activity?

POST-ACTIVITY SKILL EXERCISES

What data from Table I is used to support the statement that, "even in the presence of oxygen, proliferating rat thymocytes metabolize 90% of the glucose utilized to lactate and oxidize less than 1% of the glucose to CO_2"? Explain how the authors reach this conclusion.

Section 30

Exploring the Citric Acid Cycle

1. Produce a reading outline for the chapter in your textbook on the citric acid cycle.

2. The acetyl CoA (with 2 carbons, 2C) made via PYR DH complex undergoes a condensation with oxaloacetate (OAA) (4C) to form citrate (6C). You will find it helpful to label the number of carbons contained in each structure within the citric acid cycle. Draw a circle with the intermediate names and label how many carbons each intermediate has. Label where CO_2, GTP, NADH and FADH is produced and show the reaction of pyruvate into acetyl CoA and where it comes in and where pyruvate is made into oxaloacetate.

   - Which intermediate from the cycle is removed to make fat?

   - Which intermediate is removed to make glucose?

   - Which intermediate is removed to make glutamate?

   - Where do fats enter the cycle?

   - Write out the overall reaction of the citric acid cycle.

IN-CLASS **ACTIVITY**

Why

There are multiple points of entry and exit for carbon molecules into the central metabolic pathway of the citric acid cycle. The citric acid cycle is central to the metabolism of fats and much of glucose and many amino acids. Therefore the functioning of the cycle is critical to your understanding of integrated metabolism since many metabolites pass through the cycle.

Outcomes

1. Build specific knowledge to understand the citric acid cycle.

2. Develop your ability to transfer your knowledge from one context to another by applying prior knowledge of regulation to this new pathway.

3. Trace the carbons from acetyl CoA in this pathway and to use that knowledge to interpret ^{14}C-CO_2 data.

4. Understand the net reaction of the citric acid cycle.

Plan

1. Assign roles.

2. Reflect on your group's ability to apply prior knowledge of regulation in other pathways to this pathway.

3. Complete Critical Thinking Questions and prepare spokesperson to report out.

Critical Thinking Questions

1. Review your assignments and answer any questions.

2. Locate the ΔG values in your book for the reactions of the citric acid cycle. What are the far from equilibrium and near equilibrium reactions in the citric acid cycle?

3. Without using your book, predict at which reactions you expect regulation to occur.

4. Do the points of regulation you identified match up to branch points in the cycle? Describe the branch points (you can use your book here).

5. Discuss the regulation of citrate synthase and explain why the effectors NADH, ATP and succinyl CoA make sense.

6. Discuss the regulation of isocitrate DH and explain why the effectors NAD^+ and AMP make sense.

7. It is often said that the citric acid cycle functions catalytically. How does it resemble a catalyst?

8. The reaction PYR $\rightarrow$ OAA is anapleurotic. What does this mean? When does it operate? Acetyl CoA activates this reaction, why does that make sense?

9. Consider the reaction of citrate with the enzyme aconitase. Citrate is not chiral, yet the reaction is completely stereospecific. How is that possible?

Foundations of Biochemistry

10. Where are the oxidative reactions in the citric acid cycle? The oxidative reactions in the citric acid cycle that involve NAD$^+$ are different from those that involve FAD. How are they different?

11. The opportunity to make an ATP equivalent within the cycle occurs at one point. What is the bond breakage/bond formation reaction that results in sufficient energy to drive ATP synthesis?

12. What is still the muddiest point for your team about the citric acid cycle?

Information *Abstract excerpt from Egyed MN and Schultz RA. Onderstepoort J Vet Res. 1986 Dec; 53(4):231-4:*

"High mortality of livestock is caused annually by the plant, *Dichapetalum cymosum* (gifblaar), in the Northern Transvaal. So far no therapeutic measures have been developed for the prevention or treatment of this poisoning."

1. The toxic agent in this plant has been identified as fluoroacetate or fluoroacetic acid (FA) depending on pH. Studies on the toxic nature of FA reveal that *in vivo* FA is converted to fluoroacetyl-CoA and citrate accumulates. *In vitro* studies reveal that none of the enzymes of the citric acid cycle are inhibited by FA and fluoroacetyl-CoA is not an inhibitor of citrate synthase. Propose a reasonable explanation for the toxicity of fluoroacetate in animals that is consistent with the data.

2. The amino acid glutamate is synthesized from α-ketoglutarate, a catalytic intermediate in the citric acid cycle. In order for glutamate to be synthesized and not deplete citric acid cycle intermediates, additional α-ketoglutarate is required. Describe the NET (as in the business sense of net income which means you have more than your started with, aka profits) synthesis of α-ketoglutarate from methyl labeled ^{14}C-pyruvate in which **no** citric acid cycle intermediates are depleted (you must end up with 2 α-ketoglutarate). Show the position of the label in α-ketoglutarate. SHOW YOUR WORK.

Electron Transport

1. Produce a reading outline for the section in your textbook that covers electron transport.

2. Under standard conditions, will the following reactions proceed spontaneously as written?

   a. $2 \text{ Cytochrome c (Fe}^{3+}) + \text{NADH} \rightleftharpoons 2 \text{ Cytochrome c (Fe}^{2+}) + \text{NAD}^+$

   b. $\text{Cyto } a \text{ (Fe}^{2+}) + \text{cyto } b \text{ (Fe}^{3+}) \rightleftharpoons \text{Cyto } a \text{ (Fe}^{3+}) + \text{cyto } b \text{ (Fe}^{2+})$

IN-CLASS **ACTIVITY**

Why

The electron transport chain harnesses the energy associated with the oxidation of the electron carriers NADH and $FADH_2$ to create a proton gradient. Ultimately the energy of this gradient is used to drive ATP synthesis. Therefore it is important to understand the fundamentals of electron carriers and the energy involved in their oxidation/reduction.

Outcomes

1. Identify important roles of coenzymes and prosthetic groups in biochemistry.

2. Predict if ATP production is possible when coupled to particular reactions or processes.

3. Use $E°$ values to predict the direction of reactions and the sequence of reactions.

4. Apply general principles of electron transport to new situations.

Plan

1. Manager — assign someone be the encourager.

2. Complete Critical Thinking Questions and prepare spokesperson to report out.

3. As a group, identify any assumptions you made in solving the challenge problem.

4. Identify the most important thing you learned about problem solving today that will help you solve new problems.

Critical Thinking Questions

1. From your reading, make generalizations about the features of molecules that carry electrons in electron transport.

2. How do vitamins and minerals we eat play a role in electron transport?

3. Electron acceptors must have an E^o value that is either more negative or more positive than that of the substance from which it is accepting an electron. Which is it and why?

4. Calculate the $\Delta G^{o\prime}$ values for the reactions of the various electron transport complexes below.

   Complex I

   NADH + CoQ(oxid.) $\rightarrow$ NAD$^+$ + CoQ(red.) $E^{o\prime}_{cell}$ = 0.36V

   Complex II

   FADH$_2$ + CoQ(oxid.) $\rightarrow$ FAD + CoQ(red.) $E^{o\prime}_{cell}$ = 0.085V

   Complex III

   CoQ(red.) + cyto. C(oxid.) $\rightarrow$ cyto. C (red.) + CoQ(oxid.) $E^{o\prime}_{cell}$ = 0.19V

5. What is the $\Delta G^{o\prime}$ value for ATP synthesis? Which complexes in question 4 appear capable of driving ATP synthesis?

6. Four electron carriers, a, b, c, and d, whose reduced and oxidized forms can be distinguished spectrophotometrically, are required for respiration in a bacterial electron transport system. In the presence of substrates and oxygen, three different inhibitors block respiration, yielding the patterns of oxidation states shown in the table below. From these data, what is the order of electron carriers in the chain from substrates (meaning electron carriers) to O_2 the terminal electron acceptor?

Effects of Inhibitors on Electron Carrier Oxidation levels

Inhibitor	a	b	c	d
1	+	+	-	+
2	-	-	-	+
3	+	-	-	+

The symbols (+) and (-) indicate fully oxidized and fully reduced respectively.

7. What is meant by the term *proton gradient*? How is it an electrochemical gradient?

8. What is the sign of ΔG for the process in which protons are moved (pumped) from an area of low concentration to high concentration?

9. Why is there a negative ΔG associated with dissipating a proton gradient?

10. Which of the four complexes demonstrate the ability to pump protons from the matrix to the intermembrane space?

11. **Challenge Problem:** Archaeabacteria is an organism that converts carbon dioxide to methane by a process called methanogenesis. In this process H_2 is the donor of reducing equivalents and CO_2 is the electron acceptor. In archaeabacteria, the electron transport chain can be run in reverse. In this direction, the energy in a proton gradient is used to drive the reduction of CO_2 to HCOOH and ultimately to CH_4 rather than reducing power driving the formation of a proton gradient as in typical electron transport. The H_2 provides the reducing equivalents that are further transferred via other electron carriers. Be sure to read through the entire problem first (adapted from University of Washington final exam).

   a. Which way are the protons flowing during reverse electron transport chain? From the acidic outside to the basic inside or from the basic inside to the acidic outside?

   b. During the normal electron transport chain which way are the protons flowing? From the acidic outside to the basic inside or from the basic inside to the acidic outside?

continued on next page

c. During the normal electron transport chain (see your text) what is the trend in reduction potentials and what do the values mean?

d. From the reduction potentials provided for archaeabacteria electron transport, (see below) what is the order of electron carriers that would be involved in the transfer of electrons from H_2 to CO_2 to make HCOOH. It is not necessary to use all the reactions. Remember electron transport is reversed from the way we normally think of it since the proton gradient is the driving force. Assume each step must be driven by the flow of protons and explain your rationale briefly.

Half reactions for Archaeabacteria E'^o (V)

A. $2H^+ + 2e^- \rightarrow H_2$ -0.3

B. $CO_2 + 2H^+ + 2e^- \rightarrow HCOOH$ -0.5

C. Ferredoxin + $2H^+ + 2e^- \rightarrow$ FerridoxinH$_2$ -0.4

D. ConenzymeB-CoenzymeM + $2H^+ + 2e^- \rightarrow$ CoBSH + CoMSH 0.0

E. CH_3-CoM + $2H^+ + 2e^- \rightarrow CH_4$ + CoMSH 0.3

F. FMN + $2H^+ + 2e^- \rightarrow$ FMNH$_2$ -0.45

G. $CH_2O + 2H^+ + 2e^- \rightarrow CH_3OH$ -0.1

H. $F_{420} + 2H^+ + 2e^- \rightarrow F_{420}H_2$ -0.25

Oxidative Phosphorylation

1. Produce a reading outline for the section in your textbook on oxidative phosphorylation.

2. The following activity and skill exercise rely partially on data from a paper published in the *Journal of Biological Chemistry*.

   - To prepare, read the following summary of the relevant points of the paper.

   - [6-^{14}C]-Glc is glucose that has been labeled at the number 6 carbon with radioactive C-14. If radioactive CO_2 is produced from metabolism of such a glucose, through which metabolic pathway did it proceed?

   - What is 2,4-dinitrophenol and what is its effect on metabolic pathways?

Many metabolic experiments are performed using substrates containing radioactive isotopes such as ^{14}C. Substrates, for example glucose, can be synthesized with radioactive isotopes in known locations within a molecule. Specifically, six different glucose molecules could be made with a different carbon labeled in each position. It is known that glucose can be metabolized to a variety of products including pyruvate, carbon dioxide, and others through several different pathways such as glycolysis and the citric acid cycle. By knowing which carbon is labeled in a given experiment, scientists can learn something about metabolic pathways used under given conditions by detecting radiolabel in some metabolic end products but not others. In a typical experiment, cells would be exposed to a radiolabeled substrate for a finite period of time after which the desired metabolic product, for example carbon dioxide, would be collected and measured for radioactivity. The above-described approach is used in a paper entitled "Glucose is Essential for Proliferation and the Glycolytic Enzyme Induction that Provokes a Transition to Glycolytic Energy Production" (Greiner, E., Guppy, M., and Brand, K. (1994) *J. Biol. Chem.* 269, 31484-31490. This article is available free on the web at www.jbc.org if you wish to download a PDF of the entire document).

It is known that tumor cells have a high rate of glycolysis even under aerobic conditions. This is surprising since glycolysis typically dominates under anaerobic conditions, whereas the citric acid cycle and oxidative phosphorylation dominate under aerobic conditions. As early as the 1920's, Warburg and co-workers observed this phenomenon in tumor cells, which they called "aerobic glycolysis" Warburg hypothesized that part of the transition from normal to tumor cells resulted in damage to mitochondria, impairing oxidative phosphylation. A few years later, Crabtree and co-workers showed that addition of glucose to tumor cells results in the inhibition of oxygen consumption, a phenomenon called the "Crabtree effect". Elucidating the molecular basis of the Crabtree effect is important because understanding unique aspects of tumor cell metabolism could lead to effective, tumor-specific drug therapies.

In order to better understand which metabolic pathways are active in tumor cells, the authors of this paper use a model system, proliferating thymocytes. Although the thymocytes used in this study are not cancerous, they provide a good model for cancer cells, which have high proliferation rates. Furthermore, proliferating thymocytes have an obvious control, non-proliferating (resting) thymocytes, which behave like normal, non-cancerous cells. To answer the question, "what is the mechanism by which glycolytic enzymes are induced in proliferating rat thymocytes during the transition from aerobic to anaerobic glucose metabolism," this article looks at the combined effects of glycolysis and the subsequent fate of pyruvate into either lactate or the citric acid cycle and oxidative phosphorylation OR glucose being routed into the pentose phosphate pathway.

The method for introducing labeled glucose and detecting ^{14}C-CO_2 is as follows: The cells and an O_2/CO_2 mixture (19:1) were shaken continuously and the uptake of radioactive glucose terminated by addition of 1M $HClO_4$. The ^{14}C-CO_2 evolved was trapped in 0.5 mL of 2-phenethylamine and the radioactivity was counted. Their pilot studies showed that ^{14}C -glucose utilization and ^{14}C -CO_2 release were linear up to 3 hours.

Why

Oxidative phosphorylation harnesses the energy associated with a proton gradient created from the favorable oxidation-reduction reactions of the electron carriers NADH and $FADH_2$. The free energy of this gradient is used to drive ATP synthesis hence the name oxidative phosphorylation rather than substrate level phosphorylation. This system provides substantial amounts of ATP for cellular processes.

Outcomes

1. Understand the relationship between electron flow and ATP production in the mitochondrion.

2. Distinguish between coupled and uncoupled mitochondria.

3. Understand the interpretation of ^{14}C-CO_2 data from the article; what it reveals about metabolism.

4. Develop the abilities to identify and use diverse backgrounds of group members to solve interdisciplinary problems.

Plan

1. Form teams.

2. Manager — assign someone to be the skeptic.

3. Complete the Critical Thinking Questions.

4. This activity builds on fundamental biology knowledge and links it with metabolic pathways. Share two insights your team made about oxidative phosphorylation and its relationship with glycolysis.

Critical Thinking Questions

1. Discuss why in substrate level phosphorylation there is one ATP made for every reaction involved, yet in oxidative phosphorylation there is no reason why the ratio of ATP per NADH needs to be an integer like 3; it can be 2.7.

2. What happens to ATP synthesis in the presence of an uncoupler? Why?

Use information from your assignment and the information given below to answer questions 3–5.

One of the goals of the paper described in the assignment was to determine the biochemical basis for aerobic glycolysis observed in tumor cells (proliferating thymocytes were used as model for tumor cells). Recall that aerobic glycolysis refers to cells' preferential utilization of glycolysis over the citric acid cycle/electron transport/oxidative phosphorylation even when oxygen is available. The authors had two hypotheses. The first hypothesis was that tumor cells prefer glycolysis because not enough ADP is available to make the quantity of ATP produced in oxidative phosphorylation. The other alternative was that oxidized NAD+ and FAD are in short supply, limiting the amount of flux through the citric acid cycle. The authors used the data below to distinguish between these two possibilities.

Table I: Glucose concentration in all incubations was 4 mM. Mean values ±S.E. are given in $\mu mol/10^{10}$ cells/h from eight separate experiments.

Conditions	Glucose consumption	$^{14}CO_2$ production from $[6\text{-}^{14}C]$-Glc
Proliferating Thymocytes	740 ± 5.09	0.93 ± 0.06
+ 2,4-DNP	1240 ± 21.1	3.02 ± 0.28
+PMS	644 ± 5.29	11.7 ± 0.83

3. If ADP was the limiting reagent, what should have happened when the uncoupler, 2,4-dinotrophenol was added? What was observed?

4. PMS is an artificial electron acceptor. It can accept electrons from a molecule like NADH. If the amount of oxidized NAD+ and FAD limits flux through the citric acid cycle in proliferating thymocytes, what should happen when PMS is added?

5. What evidence supports that it is likely that [NAD+] and [FAD] limitations and not [ADP] limitations that result in aerobic glycolysis in proliferating thymocytes?

6. What would happen to the electron transport chain if one could artificially maintain the [H+] in the intermembrane space at very high levels?

continued on next page

7. Consider a reconstituted membrane system that mimics the structure of intact mitochondria in that the matrix and intermembrane space are completely intact. These membranes are formed with ONLY Complex IV and Complex V (ATP synthase) and these components are in their normal orientation within the membrane. Electrons are provided into the system via soluble reduced cytochrome c and O_2 is used as an electron acceptor.

    a. Would ATP synthesis occur? Explain.

    b. If only ATP synthase is inhibited would the spectral data of the cytochromes in this system indicate that they were all reduced, all oxidized or somewhere in between? Assume that the proton pumping is done somehow by Cyt a_3 —the last cytochrome in the complex. Explain.

POST-ACTIVITY SKILL EXERCISES

Consider the hypothetical experiment described below and apply your knowledge of inhibitors of electron transport and oxidative phosphorylation. There may be more than one right answer, but there are definitely some that are not right.

a. You have coupled, functioning mitochondria and provide NADH and O_2. If only ATP synthase is inhibited (this is not an uncoupler, instead proton movement through ATP synthase is prevented) would the spectral data of the cytochromes in intact mitochondria indicate that they were all reduced, all oxidized or somewhere in between? Explain your rationale.

b. Would the system be any different if an artificial electron acceptor was used at Complex III? Explain.

                                                 Foundations of Biochemistry

Fatty Acid Degradation and Glucose Synthesis

1. Produce a reading log for the section in your textbook on fatty acid catabolism.

2. In a healthy person, if we label palmitate with ^{14}C the label shows up in glucose. This means that in the strictest sense of the word carbon atoms from a fat are incorporated into glucose. However, biochemists say, "You cannot make glucose from fat." How can you reconcile this apparent contradiction?

Why

The carbons from fatty acids are found in glucose yet it is said that glucose can not be synthesized from fats. This activity will help resolve this apparent dilemma and understand why muscle mass is burned under these conditions. Additionally, burning fat is important for many people and we will consider how to maximize this.

Outcomes

1. Describe the relationship between glucose synthesis and fat breakdown.

2. Explain what net synthesis of glucose means.

3. Examine other effectors of fat metabolism.

4. Develop the ability to integrate your knowledge.

Plan

1. Assign roles.

2. Assign a skeptic who will ensure that your team has resolved the apparent contradiction described in the assignment.

3. As a group, reflect on your ability to integrate your knowledge about fatty acid breakdown, glucose synthesis and the role of the citric acid cycle connecting the two.

Critical Thinking Questions

1. There are 16 carbons in the starting fatty acid, palmitate, C16:0. How do the carbons of palmitate feed into the citric acid cycle? (Report structure, number of equivalents, and number of carbons for each unique product produced by metabolism of this fat.)

continued on next page

2. Do the same as question 1 for C17:0.

3. Locate the reactions in the citric acid cycle that are similar to the oxidation of fatty acids.

4. On the basis of simply counting carbons, a student proposes that 2 oxaloacetate molecules and one palmitate molecule, following the normal metabolic pathways, can be made into four molecules of glucose via gluconeogenesis. Identify and explain the flaw in this conclusion.

5. In a healthy person, if palmitate is labeled with ^{14}C the label shows up in glucose. This means that in the strictest sense of the word carbon atoms from a fat are incorporated into glucose. However, biochemists say "You can not make glucose from fat." How can you reconcile this apparent contradiction?

6. Explain why glucose could be synthesized by metabolism of a C17 carbon fatty acid.

7. How many moles of glucose could theoretically be produced from one mole of C17:0 fatty acid?

8. Muscles are made up of cells called fast twitch and slow twitch. Fast twitch muscle generally appears white while slow twitch is brown due to additional mitochondria with their ETC proteins. Muscles burn fat all the time, especially slow twitch muscle. During periods of high demand fat can only be burned so fast because there are only so many copies of the proteins and enzymes involved in ETC and oxidative phosphorylation. As a result, muscle burns glucose as we have many more copies of these enzymes. Explain why it is important that we have muscle cells that have many copies of the enzymes for glycolysis.

9. Inhibitors of fatty acid degradation are used to relieve angina (heart pain) resulting from insufficient oxygen. Why does this make sense?

10. As you may know, camels don't need to consume much water, which is why they are used in desert conditions. Where does the water come from? Be sure to consider water as a reactant and product in your answer.

11. The following quote is excerpted from NISMAT.org web site. Attempt to define the underlined segments using biochemical terminology.

> "Endurance training, loosely defined as exercise lasting 20 minutes or more, stresses the aerobic systems of skeletal muscle. Important enzymes in aerobic metabolism are <u>augmented</u> by this form of training as are enzymes involved in the metabolism of free fatty acids, by far the most energy rich substrate stored by the body. Muscles trained in this manner have a <u>greater ability to extract oxygen</u> from the blood because <u>they use it faster</u>, and they typically are more richly endowed with capillaries, the portion of the circulation which brings blood to adjacent individual muscle fibers. When muscles are trained by endurance exercise, they are contracting at a small percentage of their maximal tension. High intensity contractions, like those associated with strength training, <u>do not train the aerobic enzyme systems</u> of skeletal muscle.

The complete oxidation of glucose and palmitate to CO_2 releases considerable free energy. The $\Delta G^{o\prime}$ values are −2850 kJ/mol and −9781kJ/mol respectively. Compare the ATP yield per carbon for each of these molecules both in theory and *in vivo*. What do these results tell you about the relative efficiency of oxidizing carbohydrates and fats?

Section 34

Understanding Fatty Acid Biosynthesis

1. Produce a reading outline for the section in your book on fatty acid biosynthesis (anabolism).

2. Like most opposing anabolic and catabolic pathways, fatty acid β-oxidation and fatty acid biosynthesis occur by two different pathways. List the differences between these pathways. Include reference to location of pathway within the cell, electron donors and acceptors, C2 unit donor, and stereochemistry and the hydration/dehydration reaction. Why are different pathways necessary?

Why

We will consider a very common biochemical technique called a pulse chase experiment in order to fully understand fatty acid biosynthesis, the location of the carbons from acetyl CoA and the effects of the desaturase enzymes. This technique has been used to deduce the steps of many biosynthetic pathways.

Outcomes

1. Utilize your understanding of fatty acid synthesis to predict the location of ^{14}C carbons within a synthesized fatty acid.

2. Understand the relevance of the two naming systems for fatty acids.

3. Develop your ability to communicate solutions clearly and concisely with structures and labels.

Plan

1. Form teams and assign roles.

2. Manager — assign someone be the skeptic.

3. Complete Critical Thinking Questions.

Information

A common experiment in biochemistry research labs attempting to understand biosynthetic pathways is the pulse chase experiment. In this experiment the researcher first adds radioactively or isotopically labeled substrate (the pulse) followed by the addition of unlabeled substrate (the chase). After the molecule of interest has been synthesized, the researcher analyzes the product often by GC-MS. The fragmentation pattern will help determine the location of the labels in the synthesized compound. This allows one to know which parts of the molecule were synthesized first and which were synthesized later. Overall the information is used to propose the steps of the pathway, and design additional experiments to test the pathway proposal.

Critical Thinking Questions

1. Beginning with a supply of ^{14}C acetyl CoA labeled only in the carboxyl carbon, show the structure of the synthesized 16 carbon fatty acid, palmitate, with all the labels clearly indicated.

2. To imitate a pulse chase experiment complete the synthesis of palmitate with the first three rounds of fatty acid synthesis using ^{14}C acetyl CoA labeled as in question 1 and the remaining steps using ^{12}C acetyl CoA. Draw your product including the positions of the labels.

3. Begin with a C18:0 fatty acid. Draw the products of a Δ9 desaturase enzyme followed by one elongation reaction. Name the product using the ω system of naming.

4. Would it be possible to synthesize a Δ12 fatty acid in mammalian cells starting from a C-16 or C-18 carbon fatty acid? Explain.

5. What is the ω system name for a Δ12 C-18 fatty acid? Is such a fat essential? How do you know?

6. What is the ω system name for a Δ15 C-18 fatty acid? Is such a fat essential? How do you know?

7. If the two fats in questions 5 and 6 were consumed by a mammal and then made longer by an elongase, would the ω position change? Why or why not?

8. Explain why adipocytes (fat cells) need glucose to synthesize triglycerides.

9. Acetoacetate can be used as a fuel for cardiac myocytes.

    a. How does this substance act to fuel contraction in cardiac myocytes?

    b. Even in the presence of acetoacetate, pyruvate is required to maintain flux through the citric acid cycle. Explain.

continued on next page

10. About ninety percent of the cholesterol used in cell membranes is synthesized in the liver. The rest is obtained from dietary sources. A single enzyme controls the entry of carbons into cholesterol biosynthesis. What enzyme is it? What molecules are given to individuals to lower endogenous cholesterol production?

POST-ACTIVITY SKILL EXERCISES

Make a C16:0 FA with malonyl CoA labeled at the methylene group. Draw the structure of the FA and show all the labels.

The Urea Cycle and the Effects of Protein Degradation

PRE-ACTIVITY ASSIGNMENT

Produce a reading outline for the section in your textbook on amino acid transamination and the urea cycle.

IN-CLASS ACTIVITY

Why

The urea cycle is used to eliminate excess nitrogen. We turnover about 400 grams and eliminate about 100 grams of protein a day, hence the notion that we should eat about 3–4oz. of protein a day. This corresponds to about 5g of nitrogen. If we resupply the lost nitrogen we are said to be in neutral nitrogen balance. When we are losing protein we are in a negative nitrogen balance and when we gain protein we are in a positive nitrogen balance. Generally this corresponds to losing and building muscle mass.

Prerequisite Knowledge

A knowledge of amino acid structure, gluconeogenesis and the citric acid cycle is needed. We will integrate this information with the metabolic products of protein degradation.

Outcomes

1. Know what a transamination reaction is: the substrates used and products made.

2. Describe the strategies for recycling nitrogen and the carbon skeleton of amino acids.

3. Utilize your understanding of the amino acid structure and the function of the citric acid cycle to predict which amino acids will be ketogenic and glucogenic.

Plan

1. Form teams as instructed.

2. Complete Critical Thinking Questions.

3. Consider the urea cycle and the citric acid cycle. List two ways in which they are similar and two ways in which they are different. Your answer should address major metabolic principles, not details of molecular structure.

Critical Thinking Questions

1. Identify those citric acid cycle intermediates that are α-keto acids.

2. Is pyruvate an α-keto acid? Explain.

continued on next page

3. Vitamin B6, pyridoxal phosphate is called the amino acid coenzyme. It facilitates the removal of the amino group through a Schiff-base to make glutamate and aspartate. Which two α-keto acids are involved in the two transamination reactions in which glutamate and asparate are generated as products?

4. Alanine is used to transport nitrogen to the liver from the muscle. What α-keto acid was transaminated to make alanine in the muscle?

5. Once the alanine arrives in the liver the nitrogen is removed and transaminated onto α-ketoglutarate. What are the products of this reaction?

6. What is the first step in the degradation of most amino acids?

7. The molecules in the urea cycle are all α-amino acids. Which ones are not used for protein synthesis?

8. What step in urea synthesis is regulated?

9. Which amino acids directly provide the nitrogens used to synthesize urea?

10. What happens to the carbon fragment that remains after the nitrogen is removed?

11. Some amino acids are said to be glucogenic and some are ketogenic. What does this mean?

12. The enzymes that catalyze reactions in the urea cycle are induced during high protein diets and during starvation. Explain.

Integrated Metabolism

PRE-ACTIVITY **ASSIGNMENT**

Produce a reading outline for the section in your textbook on integrated metabolism and organ systems.

IN-CLASS ACTIVITY

Why

The five main organs systems integrated by intermediary metabolism are the liver, heart, skeletal muscle, adipose and brain tissue. While other tissues are highly important these five are the tissues we will be most concerned with in terms of integrating the pathways of metabolism.

Outcomes

1. Know the main pathways and tissue location for the synthesis and degradation of the major metabolic fuels (glucose, fatty acids, amino acids).

2. Know the main roles of the five major tissues within the context of intermediary metabolism.

3. Predict the flux through the various pathways during starvation.

Plan

1. Form teams.

2. Manager — assign someone to be the skeptic today.

3. Reflector — report a strength of your team today.

4. Complete Critical Thinking Questions and prepare spokesperson to report out. We will share responses and drawings.

Critical Thinking Questions

1. Compare the demand for glucose by the brain between the low blood glucose situation and the early starvation situation.

continued on next page

2. Under starvation conditions the body does not have incoming food and must use available stores for energy production. What are the three available stores of energy? Which will be depleted first?

3. Plot out flux vs. time (out to 2 weeks) of the pathways for protein catabolism, fat catabolism, glycogenolysis, gluconeogenesis, and ketogenesis in the liver.

4. The amino acids which are not responsible for net glucose resynthesis are somehow labeled with ^{14}C, the label will appear in resynthesized glucose. Explain this observation.

5. When proteins are metabolized under starvation conditions some amino acids are used to provide carbons for net synthesis of glucose. Which ones provide for net synthesis of glucose and are therefore glucogenic? Why do they result in net synthesis of glucose and not the others?

6. Under starvation conditions the increased operation of the pathways of protein degradation can result in the citric acid cycle intermediate α−ketoglutarate becoming depleted. When this happens glutamate is oxidatively deaminated to give α−ketoglutarate. Write the reaction. What would happen to metabolism if α−ketoglutarate becomes depleted? What is the advantage of this deamination reaction?